DEEP DOWN

DEEP DOWN

Imogen West-Knights

FLEET
2023

FLEET

First published in Great Britain in 2023 by Fleet

1 3 5 7 9 10 8 6 4 2

A CIP catalogue record for this book
is available from the British Library.

Hardback ISBN 978-0-349-72709-7
Trade Paperback ISBN 978-0-349-72710-3

Typeset in Caslon by M Rules
Printed and bound in Great Britain by
Clays Ltd, Elcograf S.p.A.

Papers used by Fleet are from well-managed forests
and other responsible sources.

Fleet
An imprint of
Little, Brown Book Group
Carmelite House
50 Victoria Embankment
London EC4Y 0DZ

An Hachette UK Company
www.hachette.co.uk

www.hachette.co.uk

For Anna

1

She drops her suitcase on an old woman's head. As it begins to tip out of the overhead locker, Billie realises that her arms aren't going to be strong enough at this angle to stop it from slipping out of her grasp. She only manages to say the words 'watch out' after the bag has hit the woman, and the sound it produces as one hard corner makes contact with her skull is appalling. The woman, who had been sitting quietly when the suitcase fell, is now bent over herself, clutching her head and making a series of distressing noises.

'I'm so sorry, I'm so sorry,' Billie says, panic rising in her chest as she feels the aura of threat radiating from passengers five rows deep in front and behind. The woman's husband gets to his feet as fast as his joints will allow and bends over her, one hand on his wife's back and the other raised in open-palmed fury towards Billie.

'What the hell is the matter with you?' he asks, and she hears his question echoed in mutters by the other passengers.

'What's the fucking hurry? Look what you've done. Look at what you've done to her.'

Billie looks at what she's done and feels her voice get tighter and tighter as she continues to apologise. What is the matter with her? It's a question she doesn't have an answer to. They had been waiting on the tarmac for about twenty minutes when she decided to reach over the elderly couple behind her and retrieve the wheelie bag. There hadn't been space to stow it above her own seat before take-off, and once the doors opened she didn't want to hold people up by having to go against the flow to fetch it. Clearly now, the right thing would have been just to wait, and go back up the plane to get her bag once everyone else had disembarked. There was no hurry. She feels heat spread up her neck and she begins to cry.

'I don't know what you're crying for,' a woman, seemingly unconnected to the victim, says. 'She's the one who should be crying.'

The elderly woman is, in fact, crying a little.

'I'm sorry,' Billie tries one more time, this apology for the crying as much as the woman's head. 'My dad just died.'

The unconnected woman gives her an exasperated look, one that seems to ask what she is supposed to do with this information. Immediately, Billie knows that this is a cheap trick. She feels its cheapness ripple through the onlookers, who continue to tut and talk about her in the third person amongst themselves. What she said happens to be true, but it is difficult to connect it to this incident with the suitcase. Still the plane doors remain closed. An aghast flight attendant is now fighting his way past the people standing in the aisle.

When he reaches the woman, he begins to administer the contents of a first aid kit.

'I'm so sorry,' Billie says to the flight attendant, desperate to endear herself to somebody, and he gives her a nod of professional neutrality. The woman appears to be bleeding. Billie stands with her eyes pinned to the floor and tries in vain to induce an out-of-body experience.

After a long time, colder air touches her face and tells her that the doors are open. Billie considers turning around to offer a final apology to the woman, who is now telling the flight attendant exactly which elements of her holiday this injury will prevent her from participating in, but she doesn't find the courage to do so. She shuffles out, dragging the suitcase behind her like a disgraced dog on a leash, clambers down the steps onto the tarmac and walks directly to the toilets to cry properly. After she is done, she sits on the toilet seat and waits until she thinks she'll be the last person from her flight in arrivals. She tips the suitcase onto its side in the cramped space of the cubicle to examine the corner for evidence of impact, but she can't find any.

The concourse is busy and Billie looks around in the vain hope that her brother has come to collect her, even though that isn't what they've arranged. She finds a quiet corner to check her phone for the directions Tom sent and to take a few steadying breaths. Twelve stops, her brother had said, on the blue line to Châtelet, and then a five-minute walk. She reads the text again to be sure she remembers it, and then also reads the follow-up text in which he had explained that Châtelet means 'little castle'. She hadn't known what she was supposed to make of this detail, and so had sent a thumbs-up

3

emoji back. There is a map on the wall next to her, which she consults. It's colourful with lines like the ones back in London, but numbered rather than named. Once she feels confident of the route, Billie weaves her way through the families and couples to buy a ticket.

Underground, she boards a packed train, and tries to reach up for the handrail at the same time as pulling down her top to contain the patch of stomach that the reaching reveals. She has a plain, mashed potato sort of a face, but it appears even more washed out than usual in the scuffed window of the train door. Sometimes when she looks at her reflection, she can see it spreading out at the edges like batter on a pan. It doesn't especially bother her. The original face wasn't all that special, if the face she left school with even was the original face. She believes that women's faces exist on a bell curve, from not quite ready up to the peak of their true, adult face, and then a slow deterioration into the faces of old age. But she doesn't know where the top of that bell curve is, for her. It's likely that she won't realise when she's there, and then she'll have missed it completely. At each station her face disappears from her view as a passenger uses a lever to throw the doors open a second or so before the train has stopped. She wonders whether this is actually dangerous or just looks it.

She receives a text.

Just asked and I can leave at 22. Meet you at the flat

She reads it twice, and wonders why he doesn't just say 10 if he means 10, then hopes it isn't a typo for 12.

4

When Billie emerges out into the city, she finds it humming with early evening energy. There is something alive in the air that makes her exhaustion more acute by contrast. She feels conspicuous on the walk to the flat, scrutinising the directions with her phone held out in front of her and pursued by the growl of her suitcase wheels.

The door into her brother's building closes behind her with a rusty screech and slam. Tom's flat is on the top floor, and as Billie heaves her bag up the stairs, she listens to her labouring footsteps echo in the stairwell. Outside his door, she lifts a scruffy mat and finds the key. It takes some jiggling in the lock, as he'd said it would, and when the heavy door swings open she follows its momentum until she is standing inside the room. Billie looks around, turning a full circle in the tiny space. She opens a door to her right, to see if there is more apartment hidden away, but it's a cupboard that contains one suit, looking like a hanged man. The shower, the hob, the bed, the sink and a small table could all be reached by stretching out a limb from the centre of the room. There is a set of French windows and six inches of balcony space that looks out onto a courtyard. A choppy sea of grey metal roof-tops stretches out, and the spires of various churches interrupt the sunset beyond.

This spartan, ill-decorated room makes Billie think of her brother as young, which is not something she's used to doing. Four years older than her, his age has always seemed massive, almost stately. Now, though, she looks at where he lives and recognises that they're at more or less the same stage of life, trudging through the featureless landscape of being twenty-something. It's a strange, un-mooring sensation.

5

The time is glaring in red from an alarm clock on the edge of the table. Tom won't be home for two hours. She pictures herself drinking a glass of white wine alone in a Parisian bar, wearing some kind of pashmina shawl her suitcase doesn't contain. The image strikes her as tragic. She'll wait for him here.

The tuna wrap she had bought at the airport but been too embarrassed to eat on the flight has gone moist and is sagging in a way that reminds her of skin. It's unappealingly warm but she eats it anyway, lingering over each wet mouthful to pass the time. Then she finds herself poking around the little room. Tom's bed is a futon on some pallets, which have partially collapsed, leaving the mattress to slope towards the floor at one corner. She recognises very few of his possessions. There's a toy pig their aunt gave him when he was small, an ugly sort of knitted hoodie he brought back from some music festival, a slumped matte wash bag. But everything else is unfamiliar. He owns eight books, and she doesn't recognise any of their names. They look like novels, and some are in French. She flicks through one of them, its margins occasionally marked with scribbled stars, and puts it back where it was. There is a diary that Billie is both tempted to read and a little repulsed by the thought of reading. She opens it a crack, but all it contains are appointments, the odd password and username.

Even though the room is tiny, there are few enough things in it to make it feel sparse. Tom has always had a talent for shedding things rather than acquiring them. Over the back of a schoolroom wooden chair, he has one of the same IKEA blankets that Billie and everybody she knows owns, except his still has the large, papery care label on it. She rips it off absent-mindedly, gathers up the packaging from her wrap and discovers a plastic bag hanging sheepishly off the cupboard door beneath the sink instead of a bin. Adrift in the middle of the largest wall there is a very small, framed line drawing of a village in England Billie is not aware of his ever having been to.

The room is cold, although the day outside is not. By the hob, there are teabags in a crushed cardboard package next to a hunk of baguette. Billie makes herself a cup of tea that is crunchy with limescale. Once she's established that there is definitely not a bathroom secreted anywhere in here, she goes exploring back in the hallway. Halfway up the next flight of stairs she finds one, although it also seems to be some kind of storage space. Sat on the toilet, wedged between a bouquet of broom handles and a broken-looking coffee machine, the image of her suitcase hitting the woman flashes before her and she lets out a pained, involuntary whimper.

Back in Tom's room, Billie inspects the bed. She decides it's relatively clean, and so she gets in under the covers. If she squashes herself flush with the wall, the sag isn't too noticeable. She gets her laptop out, puts on *Ocean's Eleven* and falls asleep very quickly.

Tom turns his key in the lock and opens the door. Inside, he finds the darkness punctuated only by Billie's face, illuminated by the screen, her mouth hanging slightly open as the tinny sound of heist music plays. He smiles and takes a picture to show her in the morning. He is tired and relieved not to have to entertain her until then. It's early enough, but

7

he might as well go to bed too. Tom changes out of his work clothes quietly, hanging them over the balcony to air out the beer and ketchup smell, and unrolls a yoga mat and a sleeping bag. He manoeuvres himself inside the bag, leans over to extract one of the thin, flat pillows from under Billie's head and then shuts the laptop.

'What?' mumbles Billie.

'Go to sleep.'

She makes a low noise in reply, and he hears her shuffle to face the wall. Tom lies awake for a while, his eyes tracing the familiar contours of the ceiling, just about visible in the dark.

2

After Tom has said goodbye to his sister, he puts his phone back in his pocket and stares out over the Seine. His breath is deep and loud in his ears. He thinks the complete sentence, *My father is dead*, then examines himself for what reaction this sentence produces. He does not find much. On a reflex, he reaches for his phone again to send a text, but catches himself. He walks on a few steps towards work, stops and turns back towards his flat. He stops again at the corner of the block. He ought to tell their mum now, while he's still numb with shock. He turns to lean against the stone wall that runs along the river, and resists the weight in his limbs pulling him to the ground. He scrolls through to find his mum's mobile number and, because she picks up on the first ring, he's not ready to speak when she answers.

'Tom? Sweetheart?'

'Mum,' he starts, wishing he'd thought about how, exactly, to navigate towards this news.

'Oh my love,' she says, her voice low and croaking. 'I'm so sorry. Mary-Jean just called.'

He rushes with gratitude that he has been pre-empted in his task, but then a more curdled set of feelings follow. To his knowledge, he has never heard his mum say Mary-Jean's name out loud, and the fact that she is sorry for his loss underlines that, to his mum, this is Tom's loss, not hers. He says nothing.

'Are you all right?' she says. 'Come home. Come and stay with us.'

Where his mum lives in Lanarkshire is not home. Tom wonders why he isn't crying. He briefly tries to make his eyes well up by not blinking. The street drowns a little in front of him and then he understands how strange and possibly even disturbed this is, and stops.

'I'm okay. Billie's going to come here.'

'Oh, good. That's good. You should be together. Whose idea was that?' He feels her deciding to cover her surprise.

'Mine,' he says.

'I could come too, it's no trouble. Do you want me to come?'

He wishes she hadn't made that the question, because he doesn't really want her to come. Now he has taken a breath, he isn't really sure he wants Billie to come either, but it's too late to go back on that now. He isn't sure why he suggested it, where that decisiveness had come from. He looks down at his free hand to see if it is shaking. It isn't.

'No, don't worry. I'll come home soon. It'll be nice to have some time with Billie.' He is appealing to her desire for them to be close, and he feels callous for knowing it.

'Okay,' she says in a soft voice, 'whatever you want, sweetheart. If you change your mind, call me.'

'Are you okay?' he asks, finally remembering to ask.

'I'm fine. Don't worry about me.'

'I have to go, I'm going underground,' he says.

'Okay, sweetheart. I'll call Billie now. And I'm here, call any time. Day or night.'

He pictures her face, sad and open, and knows he won't call.

'Love you,' he says.

'I love you too.'

Tom hangs up. Dimly, he understands that he failed at the conversation, as he so often fails at conversations with his mother. Looking back at the silent churn of the water, he weighs up his options, all of which seem bad. Then he goes to work.

When he arrives, he fobs in on the nearest till and shoots himself a pint of Coke from the gun. The pub is never all that busy during the week. He wishes it was a Saturday. He needs to have no time to think. Wayne emerges from the toilets, shaking out wet hands and grasping for blue roll. Tom hands it to him.

'You all right?' Wayne asks, peeling stray scraps of paper from under his rings.

Tom nods over the top of his glass, and gulps some Coke. It's been almost a month since he last had a drink, and he doesn't trust himself to break his resolve today. If he's not going to drink, a sugar high might help. Wayne puts his apron on over the large T-shirt and cycling shorts he wears every day. Tom has often wondered how many changes of this outfit he owns, because he always looks pristinely clean and nobody Tom knows in Paris has a tumble dryer.

'Okay, here comes the rush,' Wayne says, clapping him on the shoulders as two very old people shuffle in through the double doors.

Tom hears Noémie clomping down the stairs from the office. He sweeps his eyes across the bar to identify what she will find to complain about. She appears, scraping her anime-red hair back off her face with a headband.

'Hey,' she says, clicking her fingers at Wayne, 'limes.' She disappears into the cellar.

'Mummy it's not fair,' Wayne calls after her, as Tom goes to the chopping board and picks up a knife. 'Tom just got here, he hasn't done anything.'

'Do not annoy me today,' Noémie yells back up the stairs. Wayne grins. Winding up Noémie is, to him, a major perk of this job. He turns and sees Tom quietly slicing limes into a glass jar, then rolls his eyes.

'Well, now I look like a prick,' he says. He goes over to the till, tears off a piece of till roll and searches for a pen. He scrawls 'cheesy chips?' followed by several kisses, puts it in the dumb waiter and presses the button to send the message up to the kitchen.

'You can have some,' he says to Tom.

'Thanks.'

Wayne looks at him properly.

'What's up?'

Tom shakes his head as Noémie reappears. She picks up Wayne's phone from the bar.

'Take it away,' she says, handing it to him with disdain. 'I hate this ugly fish thing.'

Wayne's phone is housed in an over-sized iridescent rubber case in the shape of a shark. He smiles as he takes it from her and puts it screen down on the shelf below the bar, the fin on its back pointing up. Noémie gives a dramatic

12

sigh and starts pouring herself a wheat beer. The two boys wait for a moment to see if she wants to expand on the sigh of her own accord or whether she wants them to draw it out of her. The beer finishes pouring and she takes a sip. In this moment, the sentence presents itself to Tom again. *My father is dead.*

'Come on then, what's the matter with you?' says Wayne, putting an arm around Noémie. She gives a staged flinch, and then relaxes into the hug. When Noémie gets deep in a mood, she becomes a drain around which everyone's attention ends up circling. Today, Tom is grateful for it.

'I don't want to talk about it,' she says, busying herself with some blue roll and the rims of the wine glasses under the bar.

'Yes you do,' says Wayne.

Noémie capitulates immediately, taking her greying Nokia out of her back pocket.

'Fine. Look at this shit,' she says as she clicks through to her text messages. Wayne looks over her shoulder.

Tom suspects the texts are from Noémie's mother, a woman she seems to be in some kind of shattering argument with at all times, and in whose behaviour Wayne reliably takes a soap operatic interest. The dumb waiter dings. Tom throws open the doors to retrieve a pointedly small bowl of chips with a sad dusting of grated cheese over the top. He puts them down next to Wayne, who appraises them and shakes his head. Wayne goes over to the dumb waiter and sticks his head inside it.

'*Je t'aime!*' he shouts, the sound echoing loudly enough to get the attention of the two very old people now sitting in a booth on the other side of the pub looking abandoned.

13

He pauses for a moment to listen for a response which doesn't come.

'I will win this war,' Wayne says confidently, putting a chip in his mouth that is so hot he breathes through it like labour contractions, before going back to analyse the specific wording of one of Noémie's texts. They're not from her mother, but from a man she has been seeing on and off for a few months. He looks a good fifteen years older than her, though Tom and Wayne have never managed to weasel out of Noémie exactly how old he is. He sometimes comes into the pub, freshly greasy from work at his bike shop, and seems delighted by the prospect of free beers to a degree that Tom finds undignified for a man who must be forty-five.

Noémie's text drama and plotting his boyfriend's birthday party the following night provides enough intrigue to keep Wayne from probing Tom's distracted mood for the rest of the shift. And once the bar is empty, and Noémie has gone home, and the two of them have wiped down every surface, washed all the shot measures and mopped the floors, Tom tells Wayne, and Wayne is the one who cries.

Billie gets off the bus and her feet carry her back to her flat. She doesn't stop moving until she is standing in the living room, and when she comes to a halt she feels as though her whole body is humming with something like electricity. Her laptop is sat open where she had been watching television with her breakfast. A cereal-flecked bowl still stands beside it. The room is exactly as she had left it that morning, and its sameness is insulting. The flat's too quiet for Laura to be in, and she can't remember what shift pattern Bethan is on at

14

the moment. She will be asleep, either because she's just got back from the restaurant or because she needs to rest until she starts this evening. Billie doesn't want to wake her, and even if she did, something about Bethan knowing will make the day's events feel real in a way she isn't ready for. She looks at flights to Paris for two days' time and sends Tom an email containing a link to the cheapest one. Then she goes into her bedroom. She means to call her mother but instead she sits on the end of the bed and stares out of the window at a tree.

By the time Laura gets back from work, though, Billie has packed a bag. The clunk of the front door shakes her out of herself, and she realises that it's too soon to pack. She takes her toothbrush out of the bag and then stands there with it in her hand. She thinks at this moment, for some reason, of Mary-Jean's niece and nephew. Who would have told them, and what they would have thought about the news. Probably close to nothing. She feels the hideous size of the universe around her.

'Hey!' Laura calls speculatively into the flat, and Billie opens her mouth to reply but only breathing comes out. She doesn't want Laura right now. Laura, who had once thrown a farewell drinks before going on a three-week holiday. Laura who shouts when she gets home even though she knows that Bethan is sleeping. But Laura will have to do, and Billie is glad of someone to hold her when she comes out of her room and bursts out sobbing. Eventually, her crying wakes Bethan, who emerges looking smeary and confused, still wearing her jeans. She's already been at work, Billie thinks, and is alarmed by how grateful it is possible to feel for someone's company.

'What, what?' Bethan says, as Laura reaches out to rub

15

her shoulder in a way that Billie knows Bethan won't find welcome. Billie doesn't know if she can bring herself to say it again, but Laura steps in.

'Her dad died,' she says, just above a whisper.

This is the first time Billie hears these words spoken about her and it's awful. She had not wanted to break the news to Bethan, but feels strangely robbed of the moment now that Laura has taken it from her. Laura releases Billie from her grasp and Bethan moves to take over the hug. The look of hurt for her on Bethan's face shocks Billie into a deeper understanding that this is really happening. The two of them are not serious about things. Even when Bethan was savagely dumped a few years previously, it had been a dark joke from the outset; she kept bursting into laughter even as she wept in front of back-to-back episodes of *Frasier*. Now it seems they have found something they can't laugh about, and Billie lurches into frightening, unfamiliar territory.

She shares the paltry details she has about her father's death and then the three of them stand in the narrow corridor of their flat, Billie crying onto Bethan's shoulder and breathing deeply into her hair, which smells like stale oil.

'What should I do? Tell me how I can help,' Laura says after a while, the awkwardness of now being the third wheel palpable in her voice.

'Could you go and buy some beer, please,' Billie says.

'Yes, absolutely, yes,' she says, scurrying back into the pair of tasselled loafers she'd kicked off at the door and grabbing a tote bag. Once the door is closed behind Laura, they both untense a little. Bethan goes and gets two beers from the fully stocked fridge.

'What do you need?' Bethan says gently. Billie lifts her head to meet her friend's eyes. Bethan gives a small smile.

'I need to book a flight,' Billie says, uncoupling herself. She walks back into the living room towards her laptop. Bethan follows her.

'Okay. To . . . to America?' she says. Billie thinks of the city where her father lived, a place she has never been to, and the postcard generality of the image hurts her.

'No, to Paris. I need to see – Tom said I should come.'

She picks up the computer and hands it to Bethan. Bethan takes it and nods, but her face creases.

'Okay. You're sure?'

Billie wells up again and Bethan tucks her frown out of sight.

'No that's fine, we can book it for you. No problem. I just wanted to check that Tom is . . . '

Bethan pauses and Billie passes an index finger under each eye to collect the tears. Her face feels hot and swollen.

' . . . the person you want to be with. That he'll be helpful to see right now.'

On her journey back to the flat, it had begun to catch up with Billie how odd Tom's suggestion had been. Other than at Christmas and other compulsory family occasions, they don't spend time together. For many years, she had assumed it was because he was older and had more exciting things to do than hang out with his kid sister, but that had stopped being quite a good enough reason even before he was in Paris. Billie doesn't have the stability of mind to analyse why exactly she feels that she wants to be with him at this moment, but she feels it strongly. She wants to follow the feeling.

'Friday would be ideal, I just need him to confirm,' she says, and Bethan allows her to sidestep the conversation. Billie sits on the sofa, puts her head on the armrest with her eyes closed and listens to the insect click of Bethan's fingernails on her keyboard. Billie's phone buzzes and she opens her eyes to find a picture from Laura of the beer fridge at the corner shop and the message '?' underneath it. There is another message, from Tom, in reply to her email.

Sure, whatever suits

She locks her phone and closes her eyes again.

That night Billie, Bethan and Laura drink the shop beers, the fridge beers and some ouzo lurking on the top kitchen shelf. Being drunk is nice for about half an hour, but then Billie goes quiet. She knows that conversation between Laura and Bethan doesn't flow easily one on one, but she doesn't care to help them out. She sits there swaying vaguely, like a plastic frond in a fish tank, underwater and behind thick glass. When they do try to involve her, to bring her back to them, she can hear the change in the way they speak, slower and more clearly as though her English isn't quite fluent. They watch *You've Got Mail* but Billie can't follow any of the dialogue because it takes too long to percolate from her ears to her brain. Twenty minutes before the end, Laura excuses herself for her prompt 10:45 weeknight bedtime. Bethan squeezes Billie's hand in silent recognition of their joke that Laura morphs into some kind of large and frightening reptile at the stroke of eleven, and Billie tries to access the concept of a joke. She feels the day ending, but is wired by exhaustion.

Bethan puts her to bed like a child, selecting pyjamas for her and tucking her in to sleep. She sits aslant on the edge of the bed.

'Tomorrow's Thursday,' Bethan says. Bethan has Fridays off from the kitchen, so uses Thursday nights to practise techniques she needs to master to impress the more senior chefs by making dinner for Billie and Bethan's boyfriend, Ravi.

'That's fine,' Billie says.

'I'll tell them not to come, it's not a big deal.'

Billie now remembers that, this week, Angus is also supposed to be coming. Angus has transitioned from being primarily her ex-boyfriend into being primarily Ravi's best friend, and so has slowly and steadily crept back into her social life. She pictures his goofy, unguarded face. She could make a fuss, cancel dinner. But that is more effort than simply doing nothing and allowing things to continue as they would have without her dad having died.

'It's fine. It'll be a distraction.'

'Okay,' Bethan says. She gets up to leave. 'You can change your mind right up until they get here. And after that, even.'

'Could you tell them what's ... can you tell them before for me?'

'Of course,' says Bethan.

And after Bethan has closed the door behind her and Billie is finally, properly alone and able to bring the day to a close, she lies awake, unable to deny the truly unbearable thing, which is that as well as pain, she also feels relief.

3

The curtains in Tom's apartment are thin enough that once the sun rises, it is light in the room. He wakes up, but Billie shows no signs of stirring yet. She sleeps as she always has, on her front, arms pinned beside her and her face squashed up by the pillow like somebody being punched. It's relatively early, and Tom knows he should let her rest. He's starting to get used to waking up after a shift with a clear head and a whole day ahead of him. He stays lying on the mat and scrolls his phone while Billie grunts and snuffles into the pillow. Nour's face appears in his mind and he feels a kick to his chest. He looks at the time and guesses that it has been ten minutes since he woke up, which is not bad going. Ten minutes is progress.

The *nee-naw* of a police car passing the building eventually wakes Billie up. She looks around her wildly for a moment before landing on Tom and remembering where she is.

'Morning,' she croaks, reaching for a glass of water. She takes a gulp and then shuffles herself up the wall.

'Sleep well?'

She makes a 'so-so' motion with her head and drinks again.

'Your bed is shit,' she says. She presses down on the collapsed part of the futon with a foot, making it creak.

'It's not great, no.'

'You've been living here too long not to have a proper bed.'

He shrugs, neither agreeing nor disagreeing. She closes her eyes again and takes a few deep, tired breaths. Another siren passes through the room, and Tom pushes his arms out above him, his throat squeaking from the stretch.

'Do you have any nail clippers?' he says, surveying his grubby fingers.

'Why would I bring nail clippers, I'm here for three days.'

He shimmies out of his sleeping bag and gets up to search amongst his little piles of possessions. He doesn't find any, and starts biting and ripping off his nails, spitting each crescent down the sink. He looks over at Billie and catches a look of disgust passing across her face.

'So how are you, how was the flight?'

He quickly replaces the first question with the second.

'I hit an old woman in the head with my suitcase.'

'Oh. Jesus.'

'Yeah.'

'Why?'

'It just sort of—'

She pulls an imaginary suitcase out of the air and lets it fall.

'Is she okay?' he says.

'I guess so. I don't know.' She shuffles herself to the edge of his bed and places her feet on the floor one after the other. 'Would that be on the news, if she died from it? I suppose the

21

police would have to . . . ' She shakes her head like she's trying to erase this line of thinking. 'But yeah. Otherwise it was fine.'

'Good, good,' he says. He looks around his room absently. The faint sound of traffic reaches them.

'I was trying to think of what I'm going to say,' Billie says, 'on the flight. Mary-Jean asked to see a draft before the funeral.'

The final word jangles around the room.

'You're speaking?' he says.

'She asked me to, yeah.'

He nods. It makes sense Billie would be asked.

She stands up with purpose.

'Where's your coffee then?'

He points at the only cupboard, above the hob. When she opens the door, he knows that she's thinking about the mildewy smell inside, but she doesn't say anything. As Billie spills coffee granules onto the sideboard, she comes into focus for him. She has been like this since she was little, her hands not doing what she wants them to do, like she has too many of them to keep tabs on. The kettle clicks off.

'Do you want to shower?' he asks her.

She casts an eye towards the shower and he knows she's still thinking about mildew.

'Sure.'

'Cool, I'll go wait.'

She looks around the room.

' . . . where?'

'Outside.'

'Oh. All right.'

Tom nudges his feet into his slippers, seeing them

22

through Billie's eyes as a muddier shade of beige than they have ever looked before, and swings the door open and closed behind him. He sits down on the stone steps of the stairwell, and considers the fact that he hasn't thought at all about what they might do with three whole days together. As he listens to the hiss of the shower, he turns over some options. If it was a normal day off, he might go for a run, but then do mostly nothing. This is an unpleasant realisation to reckon with. There are long stretches of time these days during which nobody knows where he is. It's a thought that's uncomfortable in a way it never has been before, in his many previous years of being single. Now he can see the gaps where there is nobody to subconsciously marshal his days into productivity through their presence. Instead, his days are punctuated by images of Nour, her short fringe and long nose appearing before him unbidden, doing whatever she would most likely be doing at that time of day. Waking up, eating a meal, picking up the kids she nannies from school. He hopes that this will pass with time, but it is difficult to imagine it passing.

The noise of the shower slows to a drip and eventually Billie calls for him to come back in. She's fully dressed in a well-worn pair of wide-leg black jeans, the ends of her hair weeping water onto a large T-shirt over a long-sleeved one. She's brought her own towel, and she finishes smoothing it out over the back of his chair before crouching to investigate his fridge.

'I need to do a shop,' he says pre-emptively.

Over her shoulder he can see milk, a few stray tomatoes scattered across the shelves, a wilted bunch of coriander and a long tube of white meat. She picks up the meat and turns to present it to him.

'What is this?'

He comes over and reads the label.

'It's chicken sausage. Like a salami.'

She is holding it as if trying to touch it as little as possible.

'Is it ... good?'

He rocks his head from side to side.

'Can't remember. I guess not that good or I would have eaten the rest of it.'

She puts it back in the fridge and goes to the sink to wash her hands.

'So, why do you live in a flat with no toilet?' she says.

He smiles.

'I have a toilet. It's out there.'

'Why is it out there?'

'These flats used to be where maids would live. When people had maids that lived with them.'

'Is it cheap?'

'Not really, no. But it's central.'

Billie loses interest in quizzing him about the flat and claps her hands together, jolting him to life.

'Right! What are we doing?' She looks at the time on her phone in a managerial sort of way.

'Do you like falafel?' he says.

'Everyone likes falafel. Are you gonna shower?'

Tom thinks about his own towel over the balcony, which is one with a large picture of Donald Duck on it that their mum must have bought in the late 1990s. He can't be bothered to have that conversation.

'I'll shower later.'

He feels newly defensive about the flat, a place he spends so much more time in now than he did before, when it had been a staging area for his real life elsewhere.

They leave the apartment and Billie follows Tom as he spirals down to street level. He strides out in front of her, crossing the traffic with a practised ease. Tom has a long, loping gait that has always seemed at odds with his height, not much taller than Billie is herself. She trots a little to catch up with him.

'How's your work going?' he says, half turning to her as he walks.

'It's fine, yeah.'

'What do you actually do, when you're at work?'

Billie hears him trying to keep the judgement out of his voice, and hardens. They stop at a lamppost where Tom unlocks his bike, a ropey-looking racer.

'All kinds of stuff. Working across different accounts, assisting people, sitting in on big client meetings.'

She notices that this is more or less exactly what it says on her CV, a document she updates obsessively during the big client meetings that she is not, in fact, invited to sit in on.

'Accounts like what?'

'I move around the departments. You know parkour?'

They emerge out of the side streets onto a wide main road, Tom wheeling his bicycle with one hand around its throat.

'The jumping stuff? Is that still a thing?'

'Well, no, not really. So now there's an International Parkour Week. Because like ...'

On a reflex she takes her phone out and checks her emails.

There is one request from a senior person for her to do some photocopying.

'Yeah. Because people are over parkour. So it's to make them do it.'

'Right. So it's advertising?' Tom says.

'No, it's not advertising, it's PR.' Then, because she can't resist: 'I suppose you're the advertising expert, though.'

Tom gives a reluctant smile. A couple of years ago, he had starred in a supermarket Christmas advert alongside an animated donkey who got stage fright during a nativity play. It seemed to be showing every time Billie turned on the television that winter, and as far as she could tell, he'd been living off the surprisingly large paycheck ever since. Tom hates the advert, and hates talking about the advert, but puts effort into pretending he doesn't.

'Ah yes, of course,' he says flatly.

Billie had expected to find more of a closeness between them when she was here in person. She registers a small, familiar disappointment in her stomach.

'Well, yeah, work is good. It's mainly good to be on some kind of ladder, you know,' she says, feeling a guilty ping of satisfaction at making this dig at him.

He gives no reply other than a small, rueful noise.

'Well, here's *my* work,' he says.

They stop. On the other side of the street is a pub with white plastic chairs in front of it, hemmed in by wonky metal tables.

'Le Coq and Lion,' Billie reads.

'I know, it's supposed to be like an English pub.' She detects embarrassment in his voice that he's trying to pass off as ironic detachment. 'It's a chain.'

Billie looks through the window at this place where Tom spends so much of his time. The walls are panelled in dark brown. A black and gold flowery wallpaper spreads towards a mural of words. She makes out 'BBQ', 'craft' and 'wham!'. Below the pub's name on the front of the building, Billie sees the tagline 'authentically yum depuis 1996'. She reads it out loud.

'I think the owner's from Norwich,' Tom says.

'Do you want to go in?'

He scans the windows.

'No, it's Rico's shift.'

'What's wrong with Rico?'

'Nothing really. He recently got into beat boxing. And like, wants to show you.'

'What are the other staff like?'

'Mostly fine. A couple of them are proper friends. Oh, well, you remember Wayne, right?'

Billie has met lots of Tom's friends in passing but can't always match the faces to the names.

'Kind of, yeah.'

'He works there, and my flat was his flat before he moved in with his boyfriend.'

'Wayne. I don't think I've met a Wayne before,' Billie says.

'You've met Wayne.'

'No, I just mean it's an unusual name. *Another* Wayne, then.'

'His real name is Wei but yeah, I'm not sure he would choose Wayne for himself now.'

Inside the pub, somebody in an apron passes the window and Tom shrinks. He starts to walk again.

'Okay, food,' he says.

They turn into a labyrinth of side streets packed with small restaurants and expensive-looking boutiques. Billie feels a habitual wave of yearning to be rich, to have the kind of money that turns places like this into shops instead of scenery. Tom leads them to a hole in the wall where they buy a wrap each. They sit on the kerb to eat, hunched over themselves.

'It's good,' she says.

'Yeah, it's a thing here.'

Billie finishes her food before Tom, and being at this loose end waiting for him makes her remember why she is here. Her insides clench. She rubs garlic sauce into her sweater with spit and a thumbnail while Tom scrolls his phone, looking up things for them to do. She lights a cigarette for want of anything else to occupy her.

'You're not into art, are you,' he says, eyes on his phone.

'I like ... some art. I'd be up for seeing, like, the Mona Lisa or whatever.'

Tom scrunches his face. 'No, the Louvre is horrible. Full of tourists.'

'*I'm* a tourist,' she says, nudging a wedge of tomato into the drain.

'You're okay in small numbers.'

He gives her the choice of a French-language screwball comedy in the cinema or a photography exhibition. Neither of these seem like great options to Billie, but she wants the ease of someone else telling her what to do and where to be. She chooses photography, figuring that Tom won't need to translate pictures for her.

They rent Billie a heavy grey bicycle and she huffs through

the streets, trying to keep up with Tom, who is hunkered low over his handlebars and pedalling like he's expected somewhere. She doesn't have a helmet and hasn't ridden a bike in what must be a decade, but Tom promises her it's just one long street. Cycling along the wrong side of it adds to her sense that she is living in an eerie inversion of the real world at the moment. If she got hit by a car and died on the road in Paris, that would be the last thing anybody needed. She thinks about Princess Diana. As they pass a vast wall of vaulted windows, Tom points an arm out towards it without looking back at her, and she turns in time to catch a glimpse of the Louvre's glass pyramid through an archway.

The photography gallery looks out over a large roundabout, beyond which you can see the Eiffel Tower. Billie feels gratified by this and she asks Tom to take a photograph of her with it. He takes two pictures, in both of which the tower is underwhelming and Billie looks pale and frightened.

In the gallery, there are pictures of wide, sparse beaches; figures shot from behind moving through bright green landscapes; palm trees reflected in warm puddles. Billie watches Tom move around the rooms in the ponderous art gallery way that has never come naturally to her. It makes her lower back hurt and she doesn't know what she's supposed to be thinking about. As they wander around, she sees Tom's face from different angles and under different lights. He flickers in and out of looking like their dad. Billie has noticed this about herself recently too. Her father's face can flash across her own when she smiles, or wrinkles her eyebrows in the right way. A woman and her young son pass between Billie and a photograph, and Billie sees that the boy is filming the exhibition on a large phone. The woman turns and sees this too.

'Stop that now,' she says in a loud and pinched Home Counties accent. 'That's not how I want you to see this.'

He nods but doesn't put the phone away, and the woman turns back to the photographs.

Elsewhere in the gallery's hard, white space, Billie sits for twelve and a half minutes in front of a film about a conflict in a place she's never heard of. She notices Tom reading the exhibition notes in French, even though the English is right there, and is disproportionately annoyed by it. In the book-shop, he lingers over books about obscure topics in languages she knows he doesn't speak. She pays for a postcard of a pho-tograph, because it's one euro and she feels awkward standing there with him without buying anything. The picture shows an empty swing set under a blazing sun.

Outside, Tom asks her what she thought.

'Fine, yeah. Photos.' She lights a cigarette.

'He's a genius.'

'I'm sure you're right.'

Tom shakes his head reflexively.

'How are you so ... don't you get any emotional response to it?'

Billie thinks this is an extremely rich thing for him to have said.

'Can we not do something a bit more ... fun? Like some-thing that is fun to do, not interesting.' She puts finger quotes around the last word.

'It's not Chessington World of Adventures, Billie, it's Paris. What do you want to do?'

She tries briefly to send her thoughts out into the world and have them land on somewhere she wants to be. Then she crumples in on herself.

'I don't know. It's too hard to think.'

He softens a little. They consider and reject the aquarium. As Tom is scrolling through more options on his phone, he stops, thumb held aloft. He breathes loudly, once in and once out.

At the same moment, Billie's phone buzzes in her pocket. She taps into the email from Mary-Jean. It has a PDF attached, which she opens. There is a slightly pixelated photograph of their father, cropped in a circle from a larger image that seems to be in somebody's garden in high summer. Next to it, in a looping font that is supposed to look like calligraphy, it reads:

Celebrating the life of William Perrin
April 22, 1968–June 5, 2019

Please join us on June 16 at 2pm when we
will be gathering to laugh, cry and share
memories of our beloved William.

St Stephen's Church, Palmers Green,
London, England

They each stand there and look at the email.

'Who's the we? Us and her?' Billie says.

'I guess,' says Tom quietly.

Several cars on the roundabout blare their horns one after the other. Billie lets her eyes rest on her father's face in its strange, sombre circle.

'Okay, well, there we go. Sixteenth of June.'

She looks up and Tom has put his phone away, looking instead at something in the middle distance, or nothing at all. Billie suddenly feels run through by a deep, bodily exhaustion.

'I think I just want to sleep. Is that okay?'

'Sure, you can sleep,' he says, turning back towards her with his eyes on his feet.

They begin the cycle home, her bike even heavier than before. At the moment, there are only so many hours that Billie has per day that she can operate in, before she reaches the end of her rope and feels untethered from the world around her.

Halfway back, Tom pulls into the side of the road and Billie swerves in behind him. He turns back over his shoulder.

'Can I show you one thing?'

She'd like to say no.

'Sure, okay.'

'You'll like it, I think.'

He sets off again, Billie trailing behind him. A few minutes later he brings them to a halt outside a chapel.

'You want to go to church,' she says as they ascend the steps.

Tom turns towards her and smiles.

'I promise, even you will appreciate this.'

Billie wonders whether she can be bothered to claim to be offended while Tom buys them two student tickets. When they step inside, her breath catches. She's never seen stained glass like this. Each soaring panel streams purplish twinkling light into the space, the pillars branching out overhead like a canopy. In the high arches of the ceiling, golden stars cover a painted blue sky. They walk to two spare seats near the front of the church and look up silently for a while.

'This shits all over St Stephen's,' Billie says.

'People speak English,' he mutters, checking she hasn't been overheard, but he smiles broadly.

Making Tom laugh, even if he is laughing mostly at her, still triggers the same glow of satisfaction that she's had in these moments since childhood, a vestigial thrill. Her big brother thinks she's funny.

They sit like this for some time, the other visitors filtering past them in respectful quiet. Billie thinks about their mum, and the calm she saw on her face during the countless services she sat through next to her. Her relationship with God had made Billie feel a confusing kind of jealousy then, that her mum was so devoted to someone other than her. Now it makes her feel envious that she was so sure of something.

From near the doorway, a baby starts to cry, echoing feebly in the huge space. Billie looks at Tom as he begins to try to lip-sync the sound of the cries, contorting his face in silence to match their intonation. This was one of his party tricks for passing the time in church when they were small, and he hasn't lost his knack. A wide smile spreads on her face and for the first time since she arrived she feels sure that coming was the right thing to do.

At the front of the chapel, near the altar, there is a low rack of candles burning. Billie gets up and goes to light one herself. She slots in the only coin she has, a 50p piece, and takes a candle. Holding it up to one of the flames, she closes her eyes and tries to send some goodness to her dad, or to extract some goodness for him from somewhere, but this is a muscle she hasn't used in a long time. She chooses a moment to stop, and places her candle. When she turns, she expects to find her brother beside her, but instead she sees him far away, over the heads of tourists, waiting for her by the door.

4

It's International Parkour Week. This is a time for celebration in the office. Billie's not really working on the account other than formatting spreadsheets, but for some people on the team, International Parkour Week has been several months in the making. For this reason, Billie is eating a piece of rice paper in the shape of someone doing a forward roll from the top of a cupcake. It tastes like regular paper.

The account she does the most busywork for is the vape account. Vapinity e-cigarettes are, as far as she can tell, pretty similar to other brands except that they come in five different colours and they glow when you inhale. The company's current campaign involves trying to get cool young photographers to include a blue or green or red Vapinity as an interesting light source in their shots, in a practice everybody in the office thinks it's fine to call 'art vaping'. The less Billie has to be involved in this directly the better. She identified herself as a smoker at the start of the internship because it was a good reason to stand outside and get a break from the open-plan scrutiny of her colleagues, and so she was given a Vapinity to try out. Product research was an important part of PR, she'd been told. The one she got throbbed a bubble-gum pink and reminded her of adverts for mouth ulcer gel.

The women here with real jobs are full of ideas, pinging off each other all day long and speaking confidently on the phone. They smell expensive and wear clothes Billie wouldn't know where to buy. They're nice to her but in a glancing, surface way. There are other interns who, like Billie, are hungry for staff positions, but unlike Billie they already seem well practised in speaking confidently on the phone, smelling expensive and wearing nice clothes. Early on in her tenure, two of them who were longer-standing than her asked if she wanted to get lunch with them. Billie had said that she'd brought lunch in that day. As their faces fell slightly and they turned around to leave the office, she realised that they weren't asking her about her lunch plans so much as asking if she wanted to make some friends. She should have said yes, let her Tupperware pasta salad go claggy in her bag and made some friends. They haven't asked again, so Billie eats her lunch on a bench around the corner from the office when it's warm, and here at her desk when it's not. She spends most of her time with Martin, her direct superior, a lumpy man of about forty-five with back problems that he refers to as often as possible. He has described Billie twice as 'the edgiest person in the office', a wholly un-earned moniker which she thinks has something to do with her cartilage piercing. Sometimes, at work, she catches herself saying things like, 'Yeah, the Blackwall Tunnel is a real nightmare, isn't it?', although she couldn't point to the Blackwall Tunnel on a map and can't drive.

Billie is outside the back door of the office having a boredom cigarette ahead of the day's final meeting when her phone rings. She takes it out from the pocket of a pair of black trousers she hopes make her look professional, but she doesn't recognise the number, and lets the call ring off. She receives, skims and deletes an email from a job-hunting website. Then her phone rings again. Billie studies the screen for a moment, then slides to answer.

'Hello?'

'Billie, sweetheart.'

A woman's voice, American, but one she can't immediately place.

'It's Billie, hi,' she replies. Then she knows who it is, although the woman hasn't spoken again and is breathing deeply on the other end of the phone.

'Billie, my God. I don't—'

Mary-Jean breaks into a couple of strangled sobs, and something lurches out of place in Billie's stomach. She sits down on the edge of a concrete flowerbed and stubs her cigarette into the soil.

'What's going on?' she hears herself asking. She knows already what must have happened.

'I'm so sorry. I'm so sorry, Billie,' Mary-Jean whispers. Billie looks out into the courtyard and sits very still. They speak, or mostly don't, for about five minutes, and then Billie puts her phone back into her pocket. She gets up and begins to walk. She walks a few blocks, thinks about turning back to the office but keeps going. She reaches the river, which feels

37

like an instruction to stop walking. She obeys it. She takes out her phone and makes a call.

'Heeello?'

On the other end of the line there are car horns and other street noises.

'Tom,' she says, sounding small.

'What's up?' he asks. There is a note of alarm in his voice. Billie can't think of the last time she called him.

'What are you doing?'

'Not much really, walking to work.'

'Where are you?'

Tom falters.

'Like ... I'm – walking by the river? Why?'

'Mary-Jean called me and Dad died.' As though these two events are equally surprising.

'He died,' Tom repeats.

'Yes. She just called.'

Neither of them speaks for a moment, but Billie knows what Tom is thinking.

'Was it ... he didn't—'

'He had a heart attack,' she cuts in.

'When?'

Billie realises she doesn't know. She didn't ask, or Mary-Jean didn't tell her.

'I'm not sure. Today? I don't know.'

'And he's ... '

She can see him in her mind's eye, the confusion on his face.

' ... he's definitely dead?'

'I mean, I don't know, yes I guess so. Yes.'

Tom exhales heavily.

'Fuck.'

For several seconds, neither of them says anything. A school group passes Billie, screaming and laughing in the sunshine.

'Where are you?' he asks.

'I'm by the river. Not the same river,' she says, pointlessly. Because Tom doesn't fill the silence, she adds, 'The Thames.'

'Are you okay?' he says.

'Not really, no. Are you?'

'Mmm,' he says, noncommittally.

There is more silence, and she looks at the brown water, breathing.

'You should come here,' Tom says.

'What do you mean?' she asks, because it doesn't make sense that anything could happen beyond this present moment.

'Come and stay. Come and stay for a few days.'

'What, now?'

'Sure, why not. If you want.'

Billie looks down at her clothes, as though they will clarify something. 'But I have work.'

'I imagine they'd let you go for a few day, since—'

She listens to him find the words.

'—given the circumstances. You're only an intern anyway, how much will they miss you?'

She tries again to think about the near future, but even in this brief way it's curiously painful. Billie realises she is shivering despite the early summer warmth.

'I can't ... ' She feels a flicker of irritation. 'It'll be expensive to just get a flight.'

'We can find out. I'll split it with you.'

Billie considers arguing with him but then nods and begins to cry. She remembers he can't see her.

'Okay. Yes. Okay, I'm going to go back to the office now, and then I'm going to go home and find out about a flight.'

'Okay. Sounds good.'

She wants to stay on the phone but she doesn't want to talk any more. 'I'll call you when I get home.'

'I'll be on my shift, but call, and I'll call you back.'

Billie frowns, the phone clutched to her face. 'You're still going to go to work?'

'Oh.' Tom pauses. 'I don't know. Yeah. There might not be cover. Distracting, anyway, I guess.'

A spasm grips her insides.

'Tom,' she breathes.

'What?'

'Mum. One of us needs to tell Mum.'

They listen to each other's silence. Billie feels a preparatory anger rising. This should be Tom's job.

'I'll do it,' he says eventually, and she lets the anger melt.

'Thank you.'

She says goodbye and clicks her way back down the pavements, trying not to imagine Tom collecting pint glasses and smiling at customers in a world in which their dad is dead.

Billie walks back into the office, focusing on the rise and fall of her lungs. She feels both lightheaded and very heavy at the same time. Her phone rings, she looks at the screen and puts it back in her pocket. She can't speak to her mum now. She pushes through the double doors on her floor, putting one foot in front of the other, and she only realises when she is standing inside Michaela's office that she walked in without knocking.

40

Michaela looks up from her computer, but her annoyance turns to alarm at the sight of Billie. She must look as strange as she feels.

'I need to go home because my dad died.'

Michaela puts her hand to her chest and her bracelets clink in the quiet.

'Please,' Billie adds.

Michaela visibly re-calibrates into someone who will be evaluated later for her pastoral care.

'Of course, of course. Oh God, I am so sorry.'

Billie shakes her head but she doesn't know why.

'Just ... It just happened?' says Michaela.

Billie nods and makes a soft, weird grunt.

'Okay, of course, well, you go straight home, and don't come back. Well, no – sorry, I mean, do come back, but you don't have to. As in, come back when you're ready. Take your time,' Michaela says, gathering up, putting down and regathering a sheaf of papers on her desk.

'Okay,' Billie says. Michaela guides her out of the room and towards her desk, almost-but-not-quite touching Billie with her open palms.

'Let's get your things, and a glass of water?'

Michaela directs the second part pointedly at Martin, who launches himself up and away from his desk in wide-eyed horror that some sort of women's crisis is going on that he might be required to participate in.

'I need to get my things,' Billie parrots.

'That's it, here we go.'

Michaela stands back and in her peripheral vision Billie catches her shooing people away from the surrounding desks.

She retrieves her backpack from under her desk and puts some pens she doesn't need and her reusable coffee cup inside it. The two interns who Billie doesn't eat lunch with hover near the window, their bodies angled towards each other in silent anticipation of gossip. Martin creeps over and places a cup of water on the very edge of her desk as quietly as possible before scuttling back to the safety of his ergonomic chair.

'Okay. Thanks, Michaela.'

Michaela smiles and hands her the cup of water. Billie feels obliged to take a sip. She puts the water back down.

'Take care of yourself, anything you need—' Michaela makes a phone gesture and then clasps her hands in front of her where they can't do anything else undermining.

'Thanks.'

Billie leaves the office, feeling the eyes of the entire floor pretend not to follow her go. She takes the back stairs to the ground floor, slaps her key card onto the scanner and lets the revolving doors churn her out into the early wave of rush-hour commuters. She walks to the tube, stopping only at a corner shop to buy a packet of cigarettes that she puts in her bag next to the long-neglected vape and then forgets to smoke. As she steps onto the escalator down to the Northern line, she feels throttled by the effort not to cry, but allows some tears to fall down her face. She sits on the train, her earphones in but playing nothing, letting her eyes glaze over as she swipes mindlessly through apps on her phone. As the lift brings them back to street level at Elephant and Castle, an older woman who had been in the same carriage manages to catch Billie's eye to offer an understanding smile, and Billie feels sick at how conspicuous she is. She picks her way through roadworks and traffic lights to get her bus. As it creeps homeward, she stands leant up against the wheelchair bracket. Outside, the same streets she watches scroll by twice a day are a window onto a world she can't believe she ever occupied. She is cut loose.

5

The therapist he found online had sent Tom an address in North London, off Holloway Road. He cycles there for 4 on a Thursday afternoon, as they agreed by email. He rings the buzzer, and hears the intercom clatter.

'Hello, it's Tom? Perrin?'

There is no reply, but he hears a click and the door to the building gives way to his hand as he presses it. He climbs the four floors and lifts his head, blood pumping lightly in his ears, to find that the front door of flat eight is already ajar. Easing the door open, he expects to see the therapist, but instead he finds a low fold-out chair placed next to an umbrella stand in a hallway. Tom hovers for a few moments, until he decides that he's probably supposed to close the door and sit on the chair. It creaks loudly. The faintest smell of cooking spices reaches him, and he realises that this is almost certainly where the therapist lives as well as works. There are three other doors in the hallway, all of which are closed. His stomach drops at the thought that maybe the previous session hasn't finished, and that he will have to shuffle past some other sad sack to get to whichever room the therapy happens in. He wonders whether if he left now and changed his email address he would still have to pay for the session.

After several long minutes one of the doors opens, but in such a way that Tom can't actually see the person who has opened it. As he walks towards the empty doorway, he is half bracing himself for someone to jump out at him. When he crosses the threshold, he sees a small woman dressed in several layers of earth-tone clothing standing in front of one of the room's two armchairs and holding out her hand.

'Hello, I'm Dr Kelly,' she says as they shake, and Tom notices that she's Australian, which isn't what he expected because he now realises he was expecting the therapist from *The Sopranos*. He feels disappointed, because he thinks that there is something unserious about being Australian.

'Nice to meet you,' he says.

Tom takes a sweep of his surroundings. The room has been stripped of all personalising features. There is a wooden screen that hides a portion of the room from his view, so that all he is able to see are the armchairs, each with their own side table, and a narrow bed with a sort of Persian throw over it. He wonders what sort of state you have to be in to get to lie on the bed.

'Take a seat,' she says, and they both do so, her in the armchair closest to the window, and him in the one next to the table that has a box of Kleenex Mansize tissues on it. From this new vantage point Tom can see that there is a blue painting on the wall of the sky or the sea, or nothing.

'So,' she says, shuffling a little to tuck her feet under the chair and anchor the notebook on her lap. 'What brings you here?'

Tom looks at her knees.

'I wanted to sort of . . . '

He feels small.

'My mental health isn't good, I think. At the moment.'

'Okay.' She gives a professional smile. 'And have you had therapy before now?'

Tom shakes his head and tries to meet her eyes but it's awful and he goes back to the safety of the knee looking.

'I mean, I went to drama school, which people say is a bit like therapy. Sometimes.'

He can feel his face filling up with blood as she lets this statement hang in their air between them.

'I usually like to start by explaining a little about how I work,' Dr Kelly says, making a note of something in the book, which is artfully slanted away from Tom.

'Cool,' he nods.

'Mostly,' she says, adjusting her skirt, 'I will be listening, and you will be talking. And our sessions will be led by whatever you want to bring to them. Does that make sense?'

He nods again. He wishes he'd done any kind of prep for this.

'This is only our first session, of course, so it's not a problem if you don't know the answer, but I like to ask new patients what they hope to achieve from entering into the therapeutic process.'

A hot shame rises into his throat and he sees now that, although he had calculated that the remainder of his payment for the Christmas advert would cover fourteen sessions, what he had wanted was for this single hour to make him better. The energy saps from his limbs. A wild idea occurs to him that he could ask to be excused to go to the bathroom and then run away, but he would have to take his bag with him, which would tip her off. He doesn't know if he would even have to ask to be excused to go to the bathroom. Would she give chase? He is breathing fast. The hopelessness of this endeavour crashes over him.

The session lasts fifty minutes, which Tom spends trying and failing not to cry, failing to articulate why he is crying, apologising for crying, and wishing he hadn't come. He has described what only feels like a Wikipedia summary of his life when Dr Kelly signals that it is the end of the session by looking pointedly at the clock, closing her notebook in her lap and patting it gently with both hands. He shoves a wad of shredded tissues into his pocket and gets up. A perverse urge to hug her goodbye appears and disappears.

'Thanks very much,' he mumbles.

She does her smile again.

'Does this time each week work for you?'

He nods, knowing with total certainty that he will never see her again. He reaches around the chair to retrieve his jacket. He passes her eighty pounds in crinkled tenners without meeting her eye. The silence is unbearable.

'You got any nice weekend plans?' Tom says, as he struggles to get his jacket and backpack on.

Dr Kelly does not reply, so he looks up at her. She is smiling passively, and he realises with horror that he has crossed some sort of line. He feels his armpits tingle.

'Cool, okay, bye then,' Tom says. He rushes to get out of

the room and out of the flat so fast that he knocks over the umbrella stand as he passes it, leaving it rolling in the hallway.

He unlocks his bike and starts on his route to the South Bank as fast as the traffic will let him, imagining the wind washing him clean of his embarrassment. Freewheeling past Sadler's Wells, he pretends not to hear as a friend calls out his name. He doesn't want to have to lie about where he's been, or where he's going.

He arrives at the Portakabin that serves as the staff break room, and empties his pocketful of tissues into the bin while trying to hold open its coffee-stained lid with only the very tip of one finger. Everyone's here already, getting into costume and eating last-minute snacks. He nods greetings and pulls his costume out of a locker, a white coat and trousers covered in slashes of red paint, a filthy-looking surgical mask and a stethoscope.

Make-up is done in another Portakabin next door. The make-up artists are mostly students, though pretty good at what they do, as far as Tom can tell. He likes having his make-up done because he gets to sit down, and if he speaks too much he messes up the prosthetics, so he can sit quietly and listen to the students gossip about people at their college he will never meet. He's been cast as a doctor in the London Fright Night asylum rather than a patient, because he's a bit older than everyone else, something they can all tell. Tom makes jokes about this frequently, so that nobody else can humiliate him with it since he is already humiliating himself.

His make-up makes his eyes look red and sunken, and he usually gets a scar ripping across his neck, if he arrives there early enough. How and why all the doctors at an asylum have become disfigured no longer strikes him as a question worth asking. Not all that much thought has gone into the backstory. He had been in the graveyard area, dressed as a zombie, but he got reshuffled after one of the previous doctor guys got too drunk on the job and ended up in a fist fight with an audience member. Two or three beers while you worked was all right, in fact recommended by most of the actors, but it turned out there were some limits.

Once he's made up, he wanders back into the break room to find Rhiannon, the other person with whom he shares his zone of the attraction. Each pair of actors is assigned to a 'scarea', a patch of the trail of a few metres by a few metres wide that they are responsible for manning, and for making as frightening as they can. This is incentivised. The best scarers each week, as judged by the manager, are rewarded with 35 per cent discount vouchers for the pop-up street food event that takes place next door, and there is also a rumoured £200 reward for making an audience member shit themselves.

As scarea partners go, he has struck lucky with Rhiannon, an eighteen-year-old goth saving up for her and her boy-friend's anniversary trip to Euro Disney who is good at making enough small talk to fill up the slower afternoons, but not overly chatty. At the graveyard, he had been paired with a guy who could talk at extraordinary length about the challenges that come with maintaining a reptile collection on a budget, and who was surprised to learn, three weeks in, that they were supposed to be washing their own costumes.

He finds Rhiannon finishing off an energy drink.

'You want to warm up?' she asks brightly, adjusting the decoratively mangled straps on her strait jacket.

Starting to do voice exercises had been her idea, and it was a good one. Seven consecutive hours of screaming used to leave him with a painful, husky voice that he couldn't pull off in his real life. They walk together over to the maze of shipping containers that makes up the asylum walkthrough, running arpeggios as their breath mists in the advancing evening. Inside, it's muggy, and Tom begins to generate a sweat under his neck prosthesis that will continue until he gets to go home.

Like all shifts, it's long and spent entirely on his feet, but at least it's busy. The two of them have become pretty good at their little routines, Rhiannon attracting the guests' attention over to the darkest corner by thrashing on the gurney, so that Tom can sneak up on them from behind. Bashing the metal walls makes a satisfyingly loud noise that usually gets people going. And even if the fabled 200 quid feels out of reach, Rhiannon's pride in making dressed-up girls squeal and hide behind their large, quietly terrified boyfriends is infectious.

Before he'd started at Fright Night, he was working more or less full time at a pub. He'd applied for the bar staff position immediately after graduating, and had sensed the hand of destiny when he got the job. The pub was in the West End, right next door to one of the big theatres; a dark, oak-panelled establishment whose air was rich with the fug of decades' worth of actorly gossip, a place that glimmered each evening with the possibility of famous clientele fresh off the stage on the other side of the wall. Exactly the kind of place where a veteran director might recognise the young man pulling his pint from a Christmas advert, but then look at him more closely, see his promise and decide to catapult him into the spotlight. This is a fantasy Tom would sooner set himself on fire than admit to anyone, but lately he had started to notice that this once-delicious daydream now made him almost breathless with misery. It was pathetic. He was pathetic. And covering up this misery, which came upon him more and more while he smiled and poured beer for people he had seen on middling Netflix shows, was becoming too arduous. So he cut down his shifts there, and started working at Fright Night, where at least it was in his job description to pretend to be someone he wasn't.

Shortly after their break, which Tom spends eating a sandwich in tiny bites to eke it out over their allotted twenty minutes and Rhiannon spends watching pimple-popper videos, the unmistakable sound of several preteens screaming at the same time reaches them through the corrugated steel.

'Birthday party baby,' says Rhiannon, cracking her knuckles.

'The skeleton?' Tom asks her, lowering his voice as the crowd stomps closer.

She nods quickly and assumes her position, crouched on the ground, her arms wrapped around her knees. Along with the gurney, they have another prop near the edge of their zone, a medical students' skeleton, which you can hide behind without being spotted. Tom slots himself into this space.

A handful of wide-eyed boys creep around the corner, one of whom is wearing a badge with the number 13 on it and clutching a hot dog like he's trying to strangle it. Rhiannon starts her bit: rocking back and forth very softly, singing to herself.

Tom's never heard her do this before. She usually mumbles.

51

Perhaps this is why, instead of scuttling through like most visitors do, the boys stand transfixed for a few seconds by this unexpected gentleness in front of them. And something about these few seconds, or maybe it's just the day he's had, allows Tom to see through fresh eyes what Rhiannon is doing, what kind of a person she is pretending to be. It horrifies him.

The moment has to pass, though, because one of the bigger boys is pushing the smaller ones onwards, and this is Tom's cue to jump out, screaming with laughter, into their path. He does, and the birthday boy catches sight of him. Instantly, the child's whole body spasms. Time stands still as Tom watches the vomit jet towards him. As it makes impact, it leaves a warm slick down the front of his coat. The boy drops his hot dog and begins to cry, as an aghast woman steps out of the darkness to tend to him.

'Oh, sweetheart! Look at you, oh my—' She looks at the mess, and then looks at Tom. 'Jesus, do you have to lay it on so thick? He's a child.'

Tom is focusing too hard on not inhaling the smell coming off him to speak.

'I'm so sorry, here, let me take you out the emergency exit,' says Rhiannon, swooping in to lead the group away through the back of the building.

'Tom, will you let Sonya know?' she says, grimacing back over her shoulder at him.

Each small boy gapes at Tom's ruined clothes with open-mouthed delight as they file past him, and he hears Rhiannon's apologies continuing outside after the door has closed behind them.

He walks blank-faced back through the break room,

vampires, clowns and axe-murderers parting before him in their horror at his clothes, until he reaches the Portakabin that houses their manager's office. He knocks and enters, where he finds Sonya scrolling through Depop on her phone. She is, Tom reckons, about five years younger than him. She looks up and rolls her eyes indifferently.

'You'll need to shut down for clean-up in the asylum,' Tom says, hearing the fatigue in his voice.

Sonya barks some instructions into her walkie talkie, and then surveys him from as far away as the Portakabin allows.

'You can head home if you want, yeah?'

He nods and as he lets himself out, he has to ask:

'Will I get paid for the whole shift?'

'I'll try, just go,' she says, willing him out of her office with her eyes.

He finds her use of the word 'try' foreboding, because he suspects that, in truth, this decision is only Sonya's to make.

There is one shower on site, in which he boils himself. He stuffs his costume into three layers of Sainsbury's bags. In the hope that sharing some of his abjection might make it feel less abject, he texts a summary to Wayne, the friend he thinks will appreciate it most, along with a picture of the Sainsbury's bag. By the time he's got his shoes on, Wayne has replied.

Omfg no

NO

Tom smiles at his phone. He does up the toggles on his coat and replies.

Love my life

lmaoooo

Sorry I shouldn't be laughing but wow

Bleak

Get out of there

Yeah dw I'm being let off early

No I mean like . . . quit your job.

Quit your life lol

He sees that Wayne is recording a voice message and goes to gather up his things. As he walks to his bike, he holds his phone up to his face to listen to it. Wayne sounds excitable, talking even faster than usual.

'Okay first of all, lol, again, but more importantly – look, you should actually quit your gross job and come and live here!'

Tom is used to hearing this argument from Wayne, and switches off a little as he unlocks his chain.

'I know, blah blah excuses whatever, but, it genuinely would be perfect now because – oh yeah, news – I'm moving in with Matthias!' Wayne does a gentle mock scream. 'So my apartment needs a new tenant in the next few months, also you hate your life, rightly, and here at least you can drink nice wine and we can hang out and yeah, so you should—'

Wayne's voice is suddenly very loud in his ear.

'—do it!'

The message ends. On the cycle home Tom thinks about it in the same way he always thinks about options like this: with fear of the fact that it is possible. He tries to pull the idea out at the root. It just isn't feasible. To leave would be to admit defeat. If he lived in Paris, he wouldn't be able to go to auditions. He tries to suppress this reminder that he hasn't been offered an audition in almost six months, but the thought won't stay down. Tom knows that his failure to become an actor isn't something that requires admission. It's intensely visible. He's lit up with it. He is faintly cheered by the thought that if he did move to Paris, it would be an inarguable excuse he could give to Dr Kelly for not coming back.

With one hand on the saddle, he guides his bike into the hallway of his house, listening for the sound of voices over its ticking wheels. He registers with a dim disappointment that it's cold inside. In the kitchen, he finds two of his three housemates sat at the table in their coats. The absent housemate is a thirty-five-year-old from Spare Room that Tom has hardly spoken to and who creeps around the house with the discretion of a cat burglar.

'What did the guy say?' Tom asks Priya, who is wearing a pair of gloves and seems to be playing *The Sims* using a wired mouse attached to her laptop. She doesn't quite tear her attention away from the game quickly enough, so Stuart fills in for her.

'He said it's the oldest boiler he's seen in his entire career,' he says. 'He actually seemed kind of excited it's so old.'

'It's older than me,' says Priya, finally looking away from the screen and up at Tom.

Tom flops into the remaining chair. As soon as his legs hit the seat, he remembers what's inside the plastic bag he's carrying, but feels it would be too weird to get back up immediately and deal with it.

'They can send someone to replace it next week,' Priya says, and Tom groans quietly. He feels extremely grateful that he showered at work.

After he has sat with them long enough not to look rude or strange, Tom fills up a hot water bottle and excuses himself to his bedroom. It's in what should have been the house's living room were there not four of them living there without the landlord's knowledge. He lies down on the bed and looks around at his possessions. A meagrely populated IKEA bookcase, an orangey-brown chest of drawers that he picked up off the street, some dog-eared exhibition postcards tacked around a frameless mirror. He lies under the covers with all his clothes on and looks up at the cartography of damp and mould that constitutes his ceiling. He thinks about Wayne's message.

6

Tom is pleased that after Billie has slept for a few hours she wakes in a reinvigorated mood. She announces that she wants French food, but nothing expensive or pretentious. They cycle across the river to a crepe place Tom remembers someone mentioning once. Lately, he has taken to only going to places he's never been before, to give his life new scenery as much as possible. They sit down near the back of the restaurant, and Tom orders in French: a glass of white wine for Billie and a non-alcoholic beer for himself.

'You know she has three dogs. Mary-Jean,' Billie says.

'Okay. So?'

'It's just weird, I think. Who has three dogs? One: normal, two: normal. Three?'

'I mean, she runs a dog grooming business.'

'It's all a bit cutesy isn't it, the dogs thing.'

Before Tom has a chance to reply, Billie lets out a long sigh.

'I don't even know why I'm being mean about her. She's

really nice. And she seems to really love him which is . . . well. Which was good.'

Tom doesn't reply. He'd like to be able to change the subject, but he doesn't have any solid ideas about what the new subject should be.

'I mean, you'd have to, to put up with him,' she adds.

He murmurs in acknowledgement that she has spoken.

'So,' she says in a brisker voice, 'what happened to the girl you were seeing at Christmas? Nora?'

She's probably finishing work, Tom thinks.

'Nour. I broke it off. Wasn't quite right.' He peruses the menu.

'Oh. Shame. Isn't that the whole point of running away to Paris, to fall madly in love with some beautiful French girl?'

Tom breaks into a laugh.

'We can't sit here eating crepes in Paris and talking about love, it's too clichéd.'

'Fine.'

'Maybe you'd like to buy a beret and go to Shakespeare and Company too. We could get you an Eiffel Tower keyring if you want.'

'What's Shakespeare and Company?' she says, giving him a look of confusion mixed with obvious superiority at not knowing what he's referring to.

'It's a bookshop for tourists.'

'So not for locals like yourself, then.'

'Exactly,' he smiles. 'And I didn't run away here. I moved.'

'It's fine,' she says, flipping through the sachets in a silver pot on the table. 'If I was a failed actor working in a funfair, I'd run away too.'

58

This hurts, and his mood sours. She has never been good at walking the line between teasing and cruelty.

'I'm only joking,' she says, quietly.

There is a silence.

'Are you seeing anyone?' he says.

This feels strange to ask, though he's not quite sure why. Probably it is that, in his mind, Billie is still about eight years old.

'God no. Very much not,' she says.

Tom tries to recall Billie's university boyfriend. He only met Angus a couple of times, so he doesn't come up with much more than a face with floppy hair on top and the doleful eyes of a dog that doesn't know it's about to be put down.

'Hey.'

Tom looks up at her.

'It's nice to see you,' Billie says.

Tom wishes this kind of thing didn't make him feel awkward. Someone elsewhere in the restaurant drops a piece of cutlery on the floor. This is probably the longest time they've ever spent alone together in their adult lives.

'You too.'

'What's good then, the sweet or the savoury ones? I'm not even hungry. Have you been eating?'

He doesn't understand the question at first.

'Oh, yeah, I have been. I'm like that, though. I eat more when I'm stressed out,' he says.

'What are you having, then?'

He orders a galette with ham, cheese and an egg in it, and Billie asks for the banana and Nutella crepe despite, or perhaps because of, Tom teasing her about wanting to

order food for children instead of trying something properly French.

'Do you come here much?' she asks.

Tom looks around and shakes his head.

'Do you not have like a favourite local place? You've been
here six months already.'

'Nine months.'

'Is it nine months?'

'Yeah.'

'Well, there you go.'

He shrugs and tries not to think about Nour or to let his
face betray that he is thinking about her.

'I like to try new places.'

The waitress puts their glasses down with two neat clinks,
and Billie waits for her to retreat.

'Do you know what it feels like, the whole grief
thing?' she says.

'Mmm?' He tightens a little.

'This is going to sound weird but bear with me.' Billie
shifts in her chair and takes a sip of her wine. 'Remember
that horrible story you told me, the one about the woman
who's alone in her house and she sees a mad clown out of the
window, but it turns out she was looking in the mirror and it's
right behind her?'

Tom smiles and nods. He does remember telling Billie this
story, sat on the floor of their bedroom one night when she
was definitely too young to hear it, and he also remembers
the look of pure fear in her eyes when he had delivered the
awful punchline.

'It's kind of like ... no it's stupid,' she says.

'No, go on.'

She narrows her eyes at him slightly and then continues.

'It's kind of like, there was death in the world, and I thought I was at a safe distance from it, but it was always right there. Next to me. And the difference is that now I know about it.'

He rocks his head from side to side, considering this.

'That's almost poetic. Do you read now?'

'Fuck off, Tom,' she says, smiling, but there is a flash of hurt in her expression that makes him wish he hadn't swerved her sincerity so completely. She picks up her glass and sticks out her pinky finger.

'Look at me being poetic in a restaurant in Paris,' she says, a little too loudly, and pronouncing restaurant the French way, with three syllables and a nasal g at the end. Tom looks around and thinks he catches a couple at another table looking at them. He takes a long breath as he recognises the erraticism that precedes her being drunk.

'Don't embarrass me now,' he says gently.

'Who am I embarrassing you in front of? France?' She gestures around her with both hands at the restaurant and France by extension. There's something physically not right about her at the moment. Even when she's being light-hearted, it's like she's overflowing in some way. He can't put a finger on how it's visible that she's in pain, and it makes him uneasy.

Her phone buzzes on the table and she flips it over and scans the text.

'Mary-Jean's been going through Dad's things,' she reports to Tom, quieter now.

The phone buzzes again.

'Ohh, look.'

Billie taps the photograph and turns the phone ninety degrees on the table so they can both crane forward to look at it. It's a picture of the two of them at Legoland, aged maybe six and ten. She has a yellow plastic bucket with a Lego man's face on it over her head, two frizzy plait ends stick out of the bottom. Tom, several inches taller, is pressing the top of the bucket down, laughing as Billie fights to extract herself from it.

'I remember this. God, I could have suffocated there. Not great is it.'

Tom has never understood why Billie always wants to pore over pictures of the past, obsessed by other people's baby photos, even.

'How do you remember everything?' he says.

'Do I?'

'You always know, like, the name of someone's cousin we met once fifteen years ago.'

Billie shrugs and smiles slightly, as though Tom had meant this as a compliment. She keeps looking at the photo. Tom does remember that day, but only faintly. Lots of his memories feel less like scenes and more like colours, or flavours. Bad tastes and queasy palates.

Their food arrives. Billie gestures at their drinks to the waiter and makes a forward rolling motion with her finger, followed by a thumbs-up.

'At least say please,' Tom says, trying and failing to catch the waiter's eye to communicate his camaraderie with him.

'I did Spanish at school,' she says, shovelling more food into her mouth.

'You should work a service job. It'd be good for you.'

'Err,' she says, mouth full, 'I worked at the SU bar actually so get down off that high horse.'

'Well, then be less rude.'

She rolls her eyes at him and continues to eat. He never knows if he's supposed to give her actual advice. He doesn't understand his duties as an older brother, isn't sure whether he has any, formally. Billie wouldn't take any advice he had to give, in any case.

'Anyway, what you have to remember is that I actually have the edge over you, memory-wise, because I have memories of you from before you even have them,' he says.

Billie holds his gaze for a second and then makes a one-handed gesture like her brains are spattering out of one of her ears. 'Woah.'

'Right.'

Tom looks at his sister, increasingly flushed red and fluid in her movements. He is struck by the thought that there is now one less person in the world with whom he shares blood. That the percentage of those people that Billie makes up is now significantly higher. A faceless, cold cadaver with livid patches of blood pooling internally at its undersides muscles its way to the front of his mind. He pushes it away, and his hunger leaves him.

Soon Billie is finished, having inhaled her food and drunk her second glass of wine in gulps.

'Now what? I want to go out,' she says.

Tom looks down at his plate of food.

'Sorry, sorry. You keep pecking away at that, don't mind me.'

'You eat like there's a grenade under the table,' he says as she scrapes her chair back loudly. She goes to order another glass of wine at the bar. Tom thinks of more places they could go where he definitely wouldn't run into Nour, and lands on a bar a couple of streets away that has always looked lively but that he's never been inside.

When Tom is finished, they pay, Billie making a great show of delight about receiving a Fox's mint on the bill tray, and they leave. She lights a cigarette on the walk without breaking her gait, dragging on it luxuriantly. Tom finds it strange that she seems to enjoy smoking while walking, which for him ruins both the walking and the cigarette. Smoking is for looking around, and being looked at.

As they walk, Billie sings something in whiny cod French.

'What is that?'

She spins around and gasps at his ignorance.

'It's the song from *Ratatouille*.'

'I haven't seen it.'

'Yes you have, we watched it together.'

'Okay, well I haven't seen it in a very long time, then.'

She tuts and continues singing, waltzing solo down the pavement. He grins.

'Does it have to be so nasal? Does the rat sing it or ... '

She switches now to a familiar impression of him that bears no resemblance to him at all, in a pompous, booming voice.

'Perhaps if thou hadss't trained at draaaahma school you woulds't know how to—'

'It's here, try to look less drunk.'

Billie does her best to obey, straightening up and giving him an exaggerated wink.

The bar is small and full, every inch of the wall plastered

with posters for old gigs. It glows yellow with low light and body heat, and beyond the wide bar of deep, lacquered wood an inner room is packed with people dancing to something eighties-sounding in the spaces between tables. They get lucky and slide into a booth as two people are leaving, and Tom buys a round while Billie does a bad job of removing some of the stickiness from the places where she wants to rest her elbows with some spit and a discarded pile of napkins.

'Come on then.' She slaps the table just enough to make the glasses shake. 'What's up with Paris, why are you here?'

He hadn't realised that this was a question that Billie had, but she phrased it like it was the elephant in the room. He takes a breath to give the familiar spiel.

'They did some research and apparently your life is shorter if it's unvaried. Like, it feels shorter. People who move around a lot and do different jobs and have different relationships actually feel like their lives are longer, so their lives really are longer, in a way, than people who sort of stagnate.'

Now that it's out of his mouth the speech sounds rehearsed, an embarrassing performance of worldliness. He waits to hear her rebuttal while she takes a sip of wine, but then she swallows and it doesn't come.

'Who's they?' Billie asks eventually.

'Who?'

'They. The research people.'

'Oh. I don't know,' he says, thinking. 'Scientists.'

'But like, why Paris and not some other place. That's what I meant.'

He begins to answer but she cuts him off.

'Remember how they used to talk about when they lived here, how it took ages to get back and forth to England to see people because there was no Channel Tunnel and Dad hates flying. Always talking about how long it took or, like, the travelling, but never what it was actually like when they lived here.' She swishes the wine around. 'Weird, I think.'

In truth, he often forgets his parents ever lived here.

'They would have been your age then, I guess,' he says.

Billie widens her eyes.

'Now that is weird,' she says. Her attention is caught by something on the floor adhering itself to her shoe. He can tell she's quite drunk now, and he feels a current of affection for her that makes him feel like offering something.

'I tell you what I do find weird. About Dad dying.'

Billie looks up at him eagerly.

'I was thinking about how after all the fuss he used to make about flying, going on a plane will be one of the last things he ever does. Or that his body will do.'

At this, Billie crumples and he knows it was a misjudgement.

'Jesus,' she says.

He worries for a moment that she might cry.

'Sorry. Sorry, let's not think about that.'

Billie is staring off into space to the left of him. Then she surprises him by laughing.

'I can't believe Dad's dead in Cleveland.'

'I know. I can't really picture it. You didn't go, did you?'

She frowns, shaking her head, and is silent for a moment.

'Where was he? When he – when the heart attack happened,' Tom asks her. Billie looks down at the table and frowns a little.

'I don't actually know. It was the morning, so I've been assuming he was at school.'

Tom imagines a scene he has pictured many times before, of his dad in a shirt and tie walking down a wide, locker-lined corridor likes the ones in American high schools on television. In this image, his dad's students are always flocking behind him, like rats following the piper.

They sit quietly in the booth, letting the noise of the rest of the bar press down on them.

'I'm tired,' she says, 'my body's an hour ahead.'

'London's an hour behind,' Tom says, but Billie is already up and pawing at her coat and bag. She turns to him with a shattered look.

'I want to go home now.'

She picks up her half-full wine glass and his beer bottle and sways towards the bar to return them. She puts them down on the counter, and Tom watches her turn back and take a second squint at the label on his bottle before she pushes her way through the front door. Out on the street it's quiet, and they are exposed to the sharp wind.

'You weren't drinking?' she says.

Tom blushes.

'Not tonight, no.'

Alcohol magnifies the expression of betrayal on Billie's face.

'Why did you let me get this drunk?'

'I'm trying to cut back sometimes is all.'

Billie scrunches up her nose at him dismissively. Tom remembers that at her age he thought that the only people who didn't drink were people who were very religious or very boring, or both.

'Why didn't you say that?'

'I wanted you to have a nice time.'

'Well then have a few fucking drinks with me when our dad's just died,' she says too loudly.

He hates hearing it, something in the centre of his body recoils from hearing it.

'All right, sorry. Let's have some drinks tomorrow.'

She looks grumpy but a little appeased. She folds her arms and looks around.

'Where were those bikes?'

'I think you should sit on the back of mine.'

She shakes her head hard. Fifteen years fall off her and she looks small and lost.

'It'll hurt my bum.'

'Maybe, yes. But it's not very far.'

He watches her sway slightly.

'Okay. Don't go over bumps.'

Tom agrees, and leads her to where he locked his bike to a lamppost. He pedals them home, Billie clenching onto the flanks of his jacket and yelping at the slightest imperfection in the road surface.

Back in the room, Billie flops face first onto the bed and holds her feet in the air above her until Tom interprets that he is supposed to remove her shoes. She wriggles underneath the covers, still wearing her clothes. Tom settles himself on the mat and Nour floods through him. He tries to think of fields, of open sky and the sea to help him relax. It is hard to get to sleep now that he knows how the pattern goes, that he will wake up and her absence will hound him around the flat, sit with him as he eats his breakfast.

The day will go by, but not for any reason he thinks is worthwhile. And his dad will be dead, and the not telling Nour about it feels, in some moments, almost worse than the dying.

7

Billie sits on top of her suitcase in arrivals, looking at herself with her phone's front camera. The short, bouncy haircut had been Bethan's idea and she allows herself a moment of unfair rankling at her friend. It springs wildly away from her skull and enhances her jowls. She pulls her fingers through the frizzed curls, willing her hair to lengthen, and then locks her phone in frustration. She sees her head's new ovoid silhouette and clicks again to make the time flash up. Tom's flight should have landed by now.

There had been a suggestion that Bethan might spend this Christmas up here with them. Her parents, in the teenage giddiness of being newly retired, are on a cruise they'd been planning for years. But in the end, Bethan decided to spend the holiday with her older sister, brother-in-law and their small children. Billie has mixed feelings about this. She would have liked to have Bethan there as an additional element to disguise how strange and new this Christmas arrangement feels, even in its third year. But she also didn't want to have to translate her family for Bethan and become responsible for the vibe by default.

Eventually Tom lopes into view, wrapped up in a camel-coloured duffle coat with a sports bag over his back. He gives her an exaggerated, over-the-head wave. She smiles and returns it self-consciously, his goofy mood a welcome surprise.

'How was the flight?' she says.

'Fine. Not great that I had to fly but yeah, it was quick at least.'

'Not great how?'

'So there's this thing called climate change,' he says, smiling. It's a warm smile, and she has missed him.

'I see,' she says, nodding to play along.

'The trains were too expensive,' he continues. 'You really should have got the train, though.'

'Okay, well, that's why I flew too. The train being expensive. And it's quicker.'

'Is it really? With security and travel to the airport and stuff?' He says this in a ponderous tone, as though he's genuinely unsure and would like to know the answer. She decides not to give him the satisfaction of a debate. They come out of the arrivals hall and onto the concourse, where rain is making grey mirrors of the pavements. Billie looks at her phone. There is a text from Helen.

At Departures drop off . No rush ! H xxx

They begin to walk, and Billie prepares herself for the half-hour drive ahead. Their mum texted them an apology that it would be Helen in Helen's car collecting them from the

71

airport because her own car had some boring-sounding problem with the brake fluid. Billie has a memory of being in the car with Helen once as a child and feeling a vague unease that she realised years later was because Helen had been driving around a roundabout the wrong way.

'You got a haircut,' Tom says behind her.

She keeps her eyes forward.

'Yes, I got a haircut. It'll grow out.'

Tom says nothing and she feels his gaze itch the back of her head. She listens to the rumble of her suitcase wheels and the slash of tyres through rainwater.

'You look like a pine cone,' he says, as though reporting a neutral observation about the scenery.

'Cheers.'

She spots Helen's car, a boxy nineties Citroen. Its back end is jutting out into the roadway, hazard lights casting a red flash on a family trying to shield bags full of wrapped presents from the rain with their hands. Behind the windscreen, Billie sees her aunt's face, framed by its blur of orange hair, hove towards the wheel and squint out in their direction. Billie has the same hair texture as her aunt and her mum, frizzed and unruly, but she has always been jealous that, unlike hers, their hair is a deep red colour. Helen's, she notices now, is turning a lighter, pinkish colour at the front, a glimpse of her mum's future. As Tom and Billie move closer, Helen spots them and snaps back, giving the horn two celebratory beeps that make the mother of the family with the presents flinch with her whole body and drop her handbag. Billie waves in apology at the woman and then in greeting at Helen. She gets out of the car as they approach.

'Hello, chickens!' she says, scurrying around to the boot.

'Merry Christmas,' says Billie. She follows Helen around to the back of the car, where their aunt is trying to scrape a valley for their bags between piles of loose papers, dog bowls, raincoats, a shadeless lamp, a faded cardboard box of waffle cones and pieces of Tupperware cloudy with age.

'Chuck them in and let's get moving, I don't think I'm supposed to stop here,' says Helen.

They stow their bags, mostly on top of the mountain of other items, and Tom wriggles ahead of Billie to call shot-gun. Helen gives the boot two heaving slams which bounce the whole car, and finally on the third it catches. Billie gets in the back, and then looks through the window, which has a thin crawl of moss growing along its bottom edge, as a man in airport uniform marches out of the terminal towards them.

'Madam, for the last time, you cannot stop here. No,' he says, pointing at the car and wagging his finger in an exaggerated gesture. Helen turns towards him, smiles and gestures at the side of her head. The man looks exasperated and casts around for someone to help him. Helen shuffles herself into the driver's seat. They swing out into the road and the car groans as they accelerate away, leaving the man alone with his agitation on the pavement. Nobody speaks for a moment.

'Aunt Helen, were you pretending to be deaf?' says Tom.

She shakes her head mildly.

'Of course not.'

It's raining hard. Shop lights streak the windscreen as they swerve in and out of traffic, leaving a wake of droning horns behind them. Billie notices queasily that Helen's glasses are lying on the dashboard.

'Mum says sorry she couldn't come to do the welcome wagon,' Helen says. 'I forgot how much work hosting Christmas is so she's at home doing all the stuff I didn't realise needed doing.' As Helen veers in a crazed loop around a white van, Billie knows that this will not have been the reason their mum declined an optional trip in the car.

Helen's partner of many years had been a large, unknowable Glaswegian named Gerry. He was an airline pilot and often asleep during the day, so the few childhood memories Billie has of Helen's house are either of an eerie daytime silence, or chaos when Gerry was away on work and Helen had the run of the place. In the time they were together, Helen had usually spent Christmas in Spain, where Gerry's parents had retired to, as far as Billie could remember. When Billie was about twelve, Gerry left, under circumstances that Billie wasn't privy to but that her mum had made obvious were devastating to Helen. It had felt wrong for her to have this knowledge, at that age. It made a person of her aunt in a way that was unwelcome.

Soon, they make their way out of the suburbs. Billie notices, and Helen seemingly does not, that Tom has one white-knuckled hand gripped on the door handle and the other curled around the parking brake. When they reach country roads, Helen flicks the headlights off.

'Should we not have them on?' Billie asks in a measured voice.

'It's so you can see the headlights of cars coming the other way more easily,' Helen says soothingly. 'Everyone does it round here.'

Tom takes a large, deliberate breath and closes his eyes.

When they arrive at the house, Helen jerking the car up over a hump of earth to bring them to a stop, Billie sees their mum standing at the kitchen window. She waves, and Billie waves back. Helen gets out to fetch the bags, and Tom hovers one hand over the door release, frozen by doing something on his phone for a moment, and then gets out himself.

'Lisa!' Helen calls. 'Kettle!'

Billie watches as their mum nods, disappears from the window, then reappears as the front door swings open. She leans in the doorway, one leg crossed over the other at the ankle, the warm light from the hall escaping around her into the evening. Her hair is pulled back from her face in a low ponytail and she's wearing an apron so smeared with indeterminate staining that the pig print underneath is only faintly visible. Billie gets out of the car, her legs a little shaky from the anxiety of the drive, and enjoys the sting of cold air on her face, the absence of city sounds.

Their mum reaches out both arms as Billie hauls her suitcase towards her.

'Here are you, hello hello hello,' she sings, taking Billie's head in her hands and kissing her on the forehead.

'Hi, Mum.'

Billie rolls her bag down the hallway into the main room. Helen's house is a bungalow, with two bedrooms leading off the main hallway and the kitchen and bathroom beyond this large living area. The pair of squashy purple sofas are usually littered with blankets, abandoned slopes of magazines and vintage crumbs. Today, the cushions have been bound up in white sheets, and a pillow placed at their ends. There is a purple Quality Street on top of each pillow. Billie is touched by this, but it is also a reminder that she is a guest and this is not her home.

She parks her suitcase next to one of the sofas and takes a survey of the room. The pig thing is still going strong. There are pig cushions, china pigs on the mantelpiece, a new and menacing felt pig on the windowsill, a pig calendar by the clock that is open to July.

Tom throws his bag over the back of one of the sofas, unmoved by the pillow chocolate, and goes to hug their mother.

'Merry Christmas, sweetheart,' she says, giving his back a stroke with one hand and hooking the fingers of the other over his shoulder.

'Merry Christmas, Mum,' he says. Tom has a way of saying things like 'Merry Christmas' and 'Happy Birthday' that always sounds faintly satirical, and Billie squashes a swell of annoyance.

'How are you, my love? You okay?' their mum says, looking closely at him. Billie watches them as Tom performs a well-rehearsed trick, his eyes glassing just enough to both hold her gaze and retreat from it.

'All good,' he says as he pulls away from her and begins to kick off his shoes. 'How are you?'

'Yes, good, great.'

She says it without weight. The kettle clicks off in the kitchen and she turns towards the sound. A smell of old soup reaches Billie, and she looks around the room to greet its source.

'Martha,' she calls.

A drooping spaniel lumbers around the armchair. Billie holds her breath as she reaches down to scratch her head.

'Everyone wants tea?' comes Helen's voice from the kitchen. Billie and Tom reply yes, Billie's with milk and Tom's black, or camomile if she has it. Billie feels the stress of travel draining from her. She enjoys being here, the pigs, the dog, quiet but for the atonal tinkling of spoons on cups all day long from other rooms. She goes through the kitchen, the air warm and wet with chilli con carne gurgling on the hob, and into the bathroom. Shutting the door behind her, she smiles at the return of another memory about Helen's house. The body wash, moisturiser and tubes of toothpaste are in tiny bottles, either from hotels or branded for the airline where Helen works. Billie opens the mirrored cabinet and finds small families of shampoos from all over Europe huddled together in the darkness. She closes the cabinet and looks at her reflection. She does look like a pine cone.

Tom's voice reaches her from the kitchen, bouncy with enthusiasm.

'So what are we doing? What's the plan?'

She hears an inhalation of breath.

'God, that smells great.'

Billie frowns at herself. He's being weird.

'Well,' her mum says, following it with an efficient clap, 'we thought one present each with the carols, traditional Christmas Eve chilli, a movie and an early night.'

Billie joins her family in the kitchen.

'Unless that doesn't sound good – I'm totally flexible,' their mum adds, looking at them both and faltering. 'Whatever everyone wants.'

'Sounds good to me,' Billie says, taking her pig-pink mug from the counter and blowing into it. Their mum moves towards Billie and tucks a strand of hair behind her ear.

'Really suits you, sweetheart,' she says.

Billie looks at Tom expecting to catch a smirk, but he's looking at his phone. She watches him for a moment, his thumbs dancing. Martha flops into the room slowly, and the smell lures Billie's attention away from her brother.

'Jesus, hello.' She leans down to ruffle the dog's head, doing a baby voice, 'Hello you stinky little shit.'

'Well, look, hold on, we should be having drinks not tea,' their mum says, suddenly agitated. 'It's Christmas – here . . .'

The fridge convulses as she opens it to remove a bottle of prosecco. She obliges the pop of the cork with a little stagey gasp, and then pours. She passes a flute to Billie, one to Tom, one to Helen, and smiles around at them as she pulls the fourth in to her chest, a glass that Billie knows she won't drink. Their mum never really drinks, but to outright refuse a glass would, according to her private code of keeping things pleasant, somehow ruin drinking for other people.

'That's better,' their mum says.

Billie takes a sip and the bubbles crash against her throat.

'Now, Tom,' Helen begins in a conspiratorial tone, as he goes over to stir the chilli. 'Your mum tells me there's a girlfriend.'

Several things fall into place for Billie about Tom's demeanour over the past couple of hours.

'A girlfriend?' she says, goading. Tom's girlfriends, of whom there have been a patchy series over the years, are not things that he likes to talk about. But he turns back towards them, his face a merry red either from the heat of the food or from something else.

'Her name is Nour,' Tom says.

'Nour, lovely. And where's that from then?'

'Her family are Moroccan.'

'Oh, how nice. I love Morocco. The souks!' Helen says, throwing her hands up in celebration of how wonderful the souks are.

Billie and her mum share a smile.

'And when did you meet?' Helen continues.

'About six weeks ago. All quite new.'

'Young love,' says their mum, rubbing Tom's shoulder on her way to the fridge, her satisfaction at knowing what is going on in his love life quiet but obvious.

'Go on then, show us a picture,' Helen says.

Billie is sure that this will be too wide a window onto his inner life for Tom. But he colours more deeply and gets out his phone.

'Give me a second,' he says.

They watch him flick through to find a photograph he feels best represents her in some way to his family, and then he moves forward to stand where they can all look over his shoulder. Billie sees a picture of her brother and a small woman in a leather jacket with a short fringe. Both of them are smiling in a muted, photogenic way.

'Oh, Tom, she's lovely! Beautiful, very—'

There is a pause and Billie hears the word 'exotic' whizzing around Helen's head.

'Very beautiful. Lovely eyes,' Helen finishes. 'Well, lucky you!'

'Thank you very much,' he says, tucking the phone and the girl back into his jeans pocket. Their mum checks her watch and startles.

'Come on, we're missing it,' she says, corralling them back into the living room. 'Carols and presents, carols and presents.'

Tom and Billie remove the gifts they've brought with them from their bags. Tom lobs the parcels one by one under the tree.

'What if they were fragile?' she says.

'Okay, but they aren't fragile,' he says without breaking his flow.

They all sit down on the sheeted cushions, which seems to Billie to defeat the point of putting the sheets on at all. Their mum perches upright on the edge of the sofa, a mince pie balanced between her knees. She flicks through the channels until she finds the interior of a cathedral.

'Has everybody got what they want?' she says. 'Mince pie, more wine,' she looks to Tom, 'a piece of toast to tide you over?'

'We're fine, Mum,' says Billie. She watches their mum's face as the fret sinks back beneath its surface. There is something shameful in the visibility of her need for these Christmases to be fun, for everyone to be well and normal.

As choir boys sing 'The Angel Gabriel', their mum roots around among the gifts, sorting them into loose areas according to recipient.

'All right then, shall we have one for Billie? Youngest first?' she says, throwing a rectangular present underarm to Billie, who catches it.

'That's from me,' says Tom.

Billie could have guessed this from the fact that it is wrapped in newspaper and that it is obviously and predictably a book. She tears it open.

'Wow, a book,' she says flatly, looking down at an ancient paperback copy of *Sons and Lovers* by D. H. Lawrence.

'Open it,' Tom says, smiling. Billie opens the cover and finds a slip of lined paper with a note written on it. She reads it aloud.

'This voucher entitles Billie Perrin and Bethan Pugh (?) to train tickets to Brighton on a day of their choosing, and an ice cream each.'

Helen and their mum both express their approval at this present and Billie turns to Tom.

'You mentioned a while ago that you guys have been meaning to go, so yeah. Merry Christmas.'

It is the most thoughtful present she has ever received from him by a wide margin. Tom looks pleased with himself.

'The book was only a decoy but that's actually good as well,' he says.

'Thanks, Tom.'

She puts the voucher back inside the book and places it beside her on the sofa, yet more confused about this apparent transformation in her brother. Their mum pulls out a present. She checks the label, sees that it's for her, and tries to put it back.

'Open it,' Tom and Billie say at the same time.

'But Tom hasn't had one yet,' she protests, to sighs from everyone else that border on irritation.

'I'm twenty-six years old, Mum, open a present,' Tom says. Their mum takes the present back and flips it over with a performed curiosity, as if this package wrapped in piglet paper could be from anybody.

'Dear Lisa, Happy Christmas with love from Helen,' she reads, and turns to smile at her sister. She removes the sellotape at each end and unfolds the gift to reveal a running jacket made of a spacey reflective material. She coos.

'Much better for running on these roads,' Helen says. Billie thinks it's probably not worth pointing out that if nobody has their headlights on, she will still be invisible. Their mum holds it up to show them how it changes from reflective to matte depending on what light it catches, and Tom gives her an exaggerated nod of acknowledgement.

'Thank you. All right, now let's find one for Tom,' their mum says, burrowing back under the tree. She emerges holding a dark green parcel with a ribbon around it.

'Oh,' Billie begins to say, but their mum cuts her off.

'Dear Tom, Happy holidays, all our love from Dad and M-J,' she reads.

There is a tiny, strained pause. Their mum lifts her eyes to beam at Tom and hand over the present. The choir boys warble earnestly as Tom rips the paper. Inside, there are two turquoise, soft-looking items of clothing. He shakes them out to get a better look. A scarf and a cable knit jumper hang in the air in front of them all, their labels spinning slowly beneath.

'Wow,' says Tom in a wary voice.

Their mum takes hold of one of the labels as Tom lowers his gifts to his lap.

'Ralph Lauren! Goodness,' she says brightly. 'Lucky you.'

Billie reads Tom's almost empty expression. He would never, and will never, wear these.

'Lucky me,' he says, placing them on the floor beside the sofa. Their mum's smile is wide and firm as she inspects her new running jacket, turning it over in her hands to see it reflect in new ways.

'Mum, get one for Helen,' says Billie gently, willing the spectre out of the room. Their mum looks up as though startled by her own rudeness, and crouches back under the tree. Helen receives a wine bottle stopper with a plastic pig on the top from her friends at work, and makes a big show of being delighted with it.

Helen is cursed by two afflictions, an inability to juggle several tasks and an overambition about how many elements a meal should contain, which together mean that food in her house is always a little cold by the time it is served. When Billie sits down to her plate, the chilli is congealing rapidly alongside a brick of garlic bread that was ready to eat an hour ago, a wet-looking salad and some rice with corn in it.

'Hell yes,' says Tom warmly, touching his aunt on the shoulder in thanks as he sits down.

They are hungry and eat for a little while without conversation.

'So,' Helen says eventually, 'what's the thing you miss the most, when you're in Paris? Apart from us, of course.'

Tom meets this comment with a laugh that perhaps only Billie finds uncomfortable.

'Honestly, meal deals.'

They all laugh.

'I know that sounds tragic but it is, it's the Tesco meal deal.'

'I must say I do love a Tesco meal deal,' their mum says reverently.

Tom holds three fingers out and counts them off.

'Ham hock sandwich, Monster Munch, Pepsi Max.'

The three of them have an obligatory debate about the merits of Coke versus Pepsi that Billie can't be bothered to contribute to. Tom laughs loudly at Helen's jokes.

'No, but obviously you trade meal deals for a much better general food culture,' he says, shaking some hot sauce onto the side of his plate. 'It's amazing having all that cuisine on your doorstep.'

Billie feels that to have used the word 'cuisine' here is unforgivable and can't help but repeat it under her breath in a parodic French accent. Tom gives her a bemused look. She notices his phone light up the underside of his chin and he looks down into his lap and smiles. Billie puts the food in her mouth, chews it, swallows it down. She should relax.

'It must all be so exciting, Tom,' their mum says, grinning at him. 'Being there with all that culture. The Louvre, the Moulin Rouge, all those writers.'

Tom smiles at something private, and a few mouthfuls later excuses himself from the table to go to the bathroom. Helen and their mum discuss the ending of a television programme Billie hasn't seen while Billie drinks and repours a glass of wine. She decides to make allies of them against Tom.

'Bit rude to be texting your girlfriend on the toilet during a meal isn't it?' she says in a low voice.

'Oh, you know who I saw recently?' her mum says, breezing through Billie's comment. 'Abby Walsh's mum.'

'Oh right,' says Billie without interest. One of the only things she knows about Tom's school girlfriend Abby is that she had got married, aged about twenty, to a moderately well-known MMA fighter.

'In Morrisons,' their mum adds in an intrigued tone, as though this is an unusual place to see a person. Billie frowns.

'Here?' she says.

'Oh, no. No, in the big Morrisons off Green Lanes.'

Billie realises that she must have in fact seen Abby Walsh's mum a few years ago, not recently, but says nothing. She feels uneasy thinking about Abby Walsh. Her sister Bridget had been in Billie's year at school, and once told Billie in the queue for lunch that Abby said Tom had a bad temper, and asked Billie if that was true. She had denied it, and denied it truthfully. Tom didn't have a bad temper. But whenever she recalled that moment, something about the interaction didn't sit right with her.

'How's Abby?' Billie asks.

'Oh great, very good. She's quite high up in a marketing company now. They sell candles.'

Tom comes back into the room and puts his phone face down on the table.

'She gave me a brochure about it,' their mum continues, 'not my sort of thing but people love candles, don't they?'

'Sounds like a pyramid scheme, Mum,' Tom says, flopping back into his seat.

'No, it's nothing like that. It's candles.'

'Does she still live in Palmers?'

Lisa nods. 'They bought a house near Broomfield Park.'

Tom considers this. Unnoticed by anyone other than Billie, Martha reaches her head above the edge of the table, takes her garlic bread by the scruff of its neck and hurries away to nurse it in the other room.

'I dunno,' he says, 'I think it's a bit sad when people never leave the place they're from, do you know what I mean? There's so much world out there but she wants a house near Broomfield Park.'

'It's a lovely house apparently,' their mum says.

Billie's ripple of annoyance grows to a wave.

'Okay, but isn't Paris like, the single most obvious place to move to?' she says.

Tom looks at her with his full attention for the first time this evening. He holds her gaze for a moment with a neutral expression, and then shrugs and goes back to his plate.

'I didn't think you minded living an obvious kind of life,' he says.

The three of them look at him and Billie's face colours.

'What does that mean?' she says.

Tom catches the atmosphere changing and gives a wide smile.

'I'm only winding you up,' he says.

'Let's keep things nice,' their mum says, in a light voice.

'Deal?' Tom says, and extends his hand over the table to shake. Billie hesitates for a moment, but then takes it because she, too, wants things to be nice. She is sure to be the first to take back her hand.

'Fine.'

After the meal is finished and more wine has been drunk, they discuss what film to watch. Tom scrolls through the on-demand options. Their mum accepts and Tom considers with an open mind but ultimately rejects every suggestion that Billie and Helen make. Eventually, Helen mentions wanting to see *I, Tonya*, because Margot Robbie did some of her own ice-skating and wasn't that impressive and it won an Oscar, enough times that Tom gives up caring and allows *I, Tonya* to form a 'maybe' pile of one.

'Mum, what do you want to watch?' Billie asks.

'Oh, I don't mind, I really don't mind,' she says.

'Do you want to watch *I, Tonya?*'

'I don't mind, whatever people want,' their mum says in exactly the same tone as before, and shifts herself forward to extract a chocolate from the bowl on the coffee table.

The wine makes Billie bold, or sour.

'Can you just say what you want to watch, please?'

Lisa looks at her in surprise and with the smallest grain of hurt in her eyes.

'Let's just watch that,' Tom says, selecting the film, throwing the remote to Billie and absolving himself from any further responsibility by diving headlong back into his phone. Billie sees their mum decide not to probe this strange half-hostility from her daughter and settle back into the sofa instead. She un-peels the wrapper from her chocolate, and then eats it in three nibbles.

As Billie half watches the TV screen and half watches Tom, texting incessantly, she comes to understand what it is about him this Christmas that is making her irritated. Instead of being a vacant, half-present presence, head bent over some ostentatiously boring book, he is both more here and less here than usual. Jovial, but somewhere else in his head completely.

After about half an hour, Tom's phone rings. He gets up immediately and waits until he has stepped outside the front door to answer it. The film continues for a few minutes more.

And then, as Margot Robbie finishes looking for something inside her eighties fridge in her eighties house and turns back towards the camera, her husband punches her in the face.

Nothing in the room other than the images on the screen moves for several choked seconds. A tension deeper than muscle takes hold of Billie. She watches the film. She breathes. As the seconds lurch by, she wonders whether perhaps nothing will happen. Maybe she is the only one feeling this feeling.

'I'm very tired,' their mum says in a bright voice, abruptly standing up. 'I'll see you in the morning.'

She smiles down at Billie, who looks at her face. Her eyes are shining, but only a half light.

'On Christmas!' she says. She raises her eyebrows with an exaggerated excitement.

'Okay,' says Billie, but her mum has already turned to leave the room. 'Goodnight.'

On the screen, Margot Robbie is back at the rink, made up in glitter and sequins, spinning around and around. Tom comes back into the house.

'Where's Mum?'

'She's gone to bed,' Helen says, 'long day for everyone—'

'She got upset by the film,' Billie interrupts her. Tom looks at the screen, listening to the skates shrieking on the ice. The crowd goes wild and his brow furrows. Then, to Billie's incomprehension, he goes to follow his mother.

'Maybe best to leave her—' Helen starts to say.

'It's fine,' says Tom, and he leaves Billie and Helen alone. The film plays on in mockery of them, until Billie turns it off and they sit there in the new quiet. She cannot imagine the conversation Tom and their mum are having. Instead, she thinks of their dad. Those thoughts metastasise.

'You all right, chicken?' Helen says.

Billie takes a deep breath in and out, and remains silent for a while.

'Just not great is it,' she says, inadequately. 'That he can still make her feel like that. When he's not even here.'

Helen murmurs in agreement.

'You saw him recently, didn't you? For Thanksgiving?' she says.

'Yeah.'

'And how was he?'

An image of heaped plates appears in Billie's mind, and another of her dad laughing into a glass of wine, Mary-Jean's straight, white teeth.

'Good. Yeah, he's doing great.'

She hears, and Helen hears, the edge of bitterness in her voice.

'That is good,' Helen says.

Billie listens in to the silence of the house, through which she can't find even the distant rumble of conversation from the other room.

'You know . . . ' Helen demurs for a moment. 'It's important to remember that he suffered too,' she says.

Billie looks at her.

'He was suffering a great deal,' Helen says again. 'It helps to remember that.'

A bright anger flowers in Billie's chest.

'I know that,' she says.

'No, I know you do. I know,' Helen says in a therapeutic

tone that only riles Billie more. She feels a hardening deter-
mination not to speak. Eventually, Helen rises and retrieves
a pair of cups from the table while Billie sits there like a
stone. As Helen passes her on the way to the kitchen, she
strokes her hair.

'She's all right.'

Billie nods under her hand.

'Goodnight,' she says.

After Helen has finished clattering around in the kitchen
and gone to bed, Billie goes to the fridge and extracts a bottle
of wine. She does not decide to do it; it is merely already
happening when she pours a large glass and drinks it standing
over the sink, breathing in interrupted gulps, and then refills
it and repeats.

She goes back into the living room and prepares herself to
sleep. She gets under the blanket but her head is spinning,
so she puts a foot on the floor to steady herself. When Tom
returns she decides to pretend to be asleep out of something
like spite. She hears him rustling around in his bag, thudding
back and forth to the bathroom. Eventually, the tick of the
light switch comes, and Billie opens her eyes. All she can
now see in the darkness is Tom's face across the room, lit up
by his phone screen as he thumbs it, a wide and stupid grin
distorting his features.

8

Tom rides his bike down the canal one-handed, his free hand clutching a bunch of orange and yellow tulips. The suggestion of flowers as a birthday present for Matthias had been approved by Wayne, but he had also provided Tom with a short but strict list of flowers his boyfriend does not like. Lilies are for funerals, carnations are trashy and roses are for lovers only, according to Matthias. Tom admires this about Matthias, a particularity about things that borders on the absurd, but that Tom considers somehow continental and therefore cool. Tom had stood in front of the florists for several minutes, paralysed by the high probability that Matthias also has strong feelings about the colour of flowers, before buying the tulips because they were cheap.

Wayne insisted that being out would make him feel better than sitting at home in the shock of new grief. The bar where they are having the party is along the canal near Jaurès, and whether it will make him feel better or not, the cycle along the bustling waterfront, one of his favourite areas of the city, is a bolstering reminder that he is a real person and part of an exciting life barrelling into the future.

He arrives and tacks his way up towards the bar between groups of people until he reaches Wayne and Matthias, tapping them sheepishly on the shoulder to announce himself. He hands over his flowers.

'You are too kind,' Matthias says, kissing him twice in the air and immediately handing the flowers to Wayne.

'Wow, okay,' Wayne says, laughing.

'No, they are beautiful, but I can't hold,' Matthias says, indicating apologetically back and forth between the flowers and his shirt, which is a rich purple.

Wayne re-introduces Tom to some of his and Matthias's friends, and Tom lets himself slip into the stream of the evening, holding his lime soda in front of him like a shield. After a while, his head hurts from straining to keep up with conversations in the loud room, and he is glad when a singer with a guitar steps onto the little raised platform at one end of the room. The singer strums a speculative chord to invite some quiet. Matthias complains in a low voice that he didn't know there would be live music, but Wayne pulls the three of them towards some seats left empty by the crowd's early evening inhibition near the front of the stage. They gather around the small, poorly balanced table and look up at the singer. He's young and rangy. He introduces himself in English, spoken with what Tom thinks might be a Spanish accent, as Matthias.

Wayne gasps and leans over Tom to prod his boyfriend, who begs him with a look not to draw any attention to them. This new Matthias begins to sing in Portuguese and closes his eyes as he does so, swaying in figures of eight as he plays. Tom wishes he'd gone for a cigarette.

The song finishes. Once he has soaked up the applause, the singer takes the microphone from its stand.

'I must confess something, ladies and gentlemen,' he says in a soft rumble. 'I come tonight looking for somebody special.'

Small whoops and whistles rise around the room.

'I will sing a love song, and to sing a love song, you need someone to sing it to.'

He saunters over to the edge of the platform and stands with a wide stance to consider his options. His gaze passes towards their table and rests there.

'Ohoho, wrong choice, honey,' Wayne says as the singer locks on to Matthias and starts to move towards him.

'What is your name?' the singer says. Matthias speaks but nobody can hear him, so the singer holds the microphone down in his face. Matthias leans in slightly and his voice hoves suddenly loud into the room.

'David,' he says.

Wayne gives a loud tut. The singer retracts the microphone and smiles at him while Matthias continues to direct his gaze at floor level in the middle distance. The singer stretches out his hand and Matthias takes it with deep and total reluctance.

'He hates being touched,' Wayne says in Tom's ear with delight.

'Bonsoir, David, are you having fun tonight?' The microphone is pushed back towards Matthias's face, and Matthias hinges at it from his hips.

'Yes, thank you,' he says stiffly, and sits back again.

'It's his birthday!' Wayne shouts to the crowd. A patchy cheer comes back.

'Happy birthday, David. Your hand is sweating,' the singer says, inviting a laugh from the rest of his audience. 'Don't be so nervous.'

The microphone is away from Matthias's face so only Tom hears him say, 'I'm wearing silk' in a deadpan voice. The singer turns his eyes on Tom without releasing Matthias's hand. Wayne is convulsing with delight at his boyfriend's discomfort.

'And who is this?' the singer asks Matthias, his eyes still trained on Tom. 'He is with you?'

Matthias shrugs, a yes and a no.

The singer lets Matthias's hand go, and turns his attention on Tom now.

'Maybe you are not so scared of me,' he says to Tom, holding out his hand. Tom forces a smile and takes it. The singer sits down on the edge of the raised platform, so he can direct his song more at Tom's level. As the singer swoops and whispers his way through his next number, Tom works hard to maintain eye contact with him and Matthias nods occasionally at his own feet with a grave expression, as though listening to a lecture with which he fervently agrees. The eyes of every person in the bar burn on Tom's back. He swallows the laughter of Matthias's friends and feels sick on it. In moments like this, Tom finds it impossible to believe that he used to stand on stage and allow people to look at him, to invite that level of scrutiny. He feels separate from himself.

The song ends and Tom retrieves his hand. In the applause, Wayne puts both his arms around Matthias and kisses him on the cheek, swaddling his embarrassment. Tom gets up to go out for some air.

Outside by the water, the night is in full swing. He lights a cigarette and checks his phone. Three minutes ago, he missed a call from an unknown number. As he looks at the screen, the phone starts to ring again. He answers.

'Hello?'

'Oh hi, Tom, honey, I'm sorry, I called and then I realised it must be late there but I rang off before I could get to your voicemail and I know when you call through Skype it doesn't show the number, and so I thought maybe I'd call back and try to leave you one, a voicemail,' Mary-Jean says. His mind is stuck in the word 'honey'. He has probably only spoken to her twice before now.

'Hi,' he says.

'Is this a bad time?'

He considers this.

'No, it's fine. Are you ... how are you?'

'You know, I'm holding up,' she says in a voice thick with emotion. 'I'm blessed to be here with some dear friends and family who are taking good care of me.'

'That's good,' he says. A woman waves for his attention and makes a lighter gesture. He hands it over and she thanks him.

'And how are you doing? Sounds like you're out with some friends?'

'Yeah. I'm at a birthday party,' he tells her for some reason.

'Oh great, that's good that you're doing that. We've just got to keep going, don't we?'

'Mmm.'

'So – okay, the reason I called is because I wanted to ask

95

you something, just because you know, I wasn't sure it would be appropriate to get in touch directly with your mom about this, I don't want to bother her again after, after we already spoke before,' she says.

Tom wonders now why she has called him and not Billie. He has a queasy feeling that the decision was driven by some sense that he might feel left out if she called Billie again.

'Okay, shoot,' he says, a phrase he has never said before.

'So, your dad, I don't know whether you know this, I guess it's not the kind of thing fathers and sons talk about.' Mary-Jean laughs nervously. Tom doesn't know what fathers and sons talk about. 'But he told me once that he wanted to be buried in England, to have the funeral and everything in England when he – when he passed on. And I know you kids went to church a lot, right? In Palms Green?'

'Palmers Green,' Tom corrects her.

'Sorry, honey, yes, Palmers Green. And the church is near where he used to teach too, isn't it, so what I'm asking is do you think – that would be a good place to have it, right? Don't you think?'

The suggestion makes several things too real, too quickly. He looks around at the people on the canal, and the wrongness of everything is stark and gruesome.

'Would that be nice for you guys?' she asks, a little plaintive against his silence.

'Yep. Sounds good,' he says. 'Thanks for … thanks for calling.'

'Okay. Okay great, well I'll get on with the arrangements,' she says with the particular kind of organisational bluster that only the recently devastated have.

'Thanks,' he says again. He wishes he wanted to offer to help her.

'Take care now, speak soon, try to have a little fun okay?'

'Okay,' he says.

'Bye now,' she says.

Tom hangs up and immediately turns his phone off.

It feels impossible that he will return to the party, and so he doesn't. Instead, Tom walks along the river for several blocks, unable to isolate any meaning in the noise crowding his mind. He hits his forehead with the heel of his hand experimentally, which instantly seems absurd, then stumbles over a jutting edge of paving stone, giving him a rush of embarrassment all the more pronounced for having nobody there to witness it. He continues to walk. After what the aching of his feet tells him is a long time, a woman cycles past him slightly too close and he remembers that he took his bike to the bar. He stops sharply. It's not unthinkably far to walk back, but the idea of having to do so is unbearable. Tom stands by a bridge he doesn't recognise for a moment, allowing the impotence of this stupid little excursion to expand around him. He'll get his bike in the morning. He should go home.

When he finally arrives back at his building an hour or so later and has tramped his humiliation up five flights, he finds Wayne in the corridor outside his apartment, his shark phone clamped on his ear. As soon as Wayne spots him, he hangs up with a conspicuous eye roll.

'Right, okay well, thanks for that,' he says, putting the phone back in the bum bag at his waist. 'You can't disappear the day after your dad dies and expect me to be like, okay cool, bye then.' The speed at which Wayne is speaking tells Tom how worried he has been.

'I'm sorry,' Tom says, and means it. He feels ashamed of what now strikes him as his childish performance of being upset, an inarticulate piece of tantrum theatre.

'It's fine,' Wayne says dismissively. 'I called you. What's going on with your phone?'

'It's out of battery,' Tom lies.

'Look I know you're having a bad time but like ... this habit sucks.' Wayne suddenly laughs with relief and Tom finds himself smiling automatically and without feeling. 'The vanishing act thing. Maybe we could lose that.'

'I didn't mean to freak you out,' Tom says, the sediment of self-loathing coming to rest in his stomach. 'I'm sorry.'

'Okay, well. The least you can do is offer me a drink.'

They switch places on the mat in front of his apartment. As he fiddles with the key in the door, Tom prepares for the moment when Wayne sees what's on the other side. Wayne's intake of breath when the door swings wide is more awful for his trying to suppress it. Tom sees his flat through someone else's eyes and it is an unpleasant view. There are clothes flung on the floor, bedding strewn in fretful bunches around the room and a developing funk of old dishes. Four listless flies orbit each other in the middle of the space. He looks around at the scene and has to admit that while his mood lately is not to do with the flat, it can't be helping.

'I think this is all I have,' Tom says, ploughing his way through the mess and redistributing the flies in the process. He extracts a single can of room-temperature Breton cider from the cupboard. When he turns back to Wayne with the can, Tom sees a look of pity that makes his skin creep.

'You know, I'm all right, thank you,' Wayne says.

Tom watches as the flies regroup near the window.

'I'm gonna do some cleaning up now, I think,' he says, 'before Billie comes.'

'Okay, great. Good.'

'It's a bit depressing isn't it, like this,' Tom says, because he can't bear for it to be unspoken any longer.

'A bit, yeah,' Wayne says. 'Do you want some help?'

Tom suspects that the layers beneath what is immediately visible might be even more repellent. He thinks darkly of a half-eaten plate of fajitas he doesn't remember clearing.

'No no, thanks. I'm fine. Tell Matthias I'm sorry about tonight.'

'Tell him yourself, you lazy fuck,' Wayne says warmly.

'Yes. Okay yes, I will.'

Wayne smooths his jacket down and opens the front door. As he does so, Tom is reminded of the canvas bag slouched beside it.

'Oh,' he says, and reaches for the bag, 'can you take this with you?'

Wayne takes it from him.

'And hold on to it for a bit or something.'

Wayne looks inside at the jumper, a book, a sad handful of hair clips.

'Sure,' he says.

'It's just some of Nour's stuff,' a knot tightens in Tom's throat but he swallows through it, 'and I don't want Billie grilling me over it. She's nosy.'

Wayne slings the bag over his shoulder.

'All right. Get some rest,' he says, and slips out, shutting the door gently behind him.

Tom looks around the room. He bends down to scoop some of the clothes onto his chair, and leans against the table to start sorting them. He picks up each item and brings it to his nose, pressing the crotch of his underwear and the armpits of his T-shirts to his face and then discarding them into piles, a large dirty one and a smaller pile he is charitably thinking of as clean. His phone buzzes.

I could give the stuff back to her if you want, I have her number

Tom holds his thumbs over the screen. He doesn't like to think about the two of them meeting, talking about him to each other.

Keep it for now, but thanks

He puts his phone down and turns back to his sorting. One item after another lands in the same place. Dirty, dirty, dirty.

'I mean it's a little unusual but not, like, concerningly weird,' says Angus, 'no?'

He looks around the table at Billie, Bethan and Ravi for confirmation. Ravi tips his head in a maybe motion, Bethan shrugs and stifles a yawn, and Billie doesn't find it in herself to respond at all. Laura holds her mouth lolled open in a caricature of disagreement.

'I'm sorry, yes it is. It is weird. I am a twenty-three-year-old woman. If I have,' she breaks briefly into a stage whisper, '*sex with a guy I do not expect to wake up in the night and find him gaming next to me.*'

Laura says the word gaming as though it is a euphemism for masturbation.

'Was it on like, a games console? Or his phone?' Angus asks. He moves some final humps of mashed potato around his plate in contemplation of eating yet more of it and then puts down his fork in defeat.

'You can only play Mario Kart on Switch,' Ravi cuts across Laura to inform them with an air of expert knowledge. 'Unless he still has an older console. It wasn't a Nintendo DS, was it?' He looks perturbed. 'That would actually be a bit weird.'

'I don't know what it was, I don't recognise different Gameboys,' says Laura, not enjoying that her story about being woken up by the frenetic noise of a pixelated car race is not landing the way she'd expected. Billie breathes deeply. Laura is always around for these dinners, even though she doesn't seem to like Angus or Ravi all that much, which Billie thinks comes from a fear of being left out of anything, including events she doesn't actually want to attend. Billie finds Angus's presence these days, a good few years now after they broke up, more or less unremarkable. Ravi has always talked too much and too loudly, but is visibly obsessed with Bethan, which means Billie has no choice but to think of him fondly. In any case, she's happy to have someone here to dominate the conversation and make her silence more palatable. Earlier on, she'd found she was able to ride the wave because there was food to eat and people to entertain, but now she has washed up cold and shivering on the shore of the evening, drained of energy. It has been a strange day. She spoke to her mum for a while, then walked in a circular stupor around her neighbourhood, buying things she needed, mundane anchors like milk and make-up wipes. There is a blank space for several hours in the middle of the day, and then a period in which she made herself horrified looking at a photo gallery of 9/11 and drank half a litre of juice in a flavour she'd never bought before: guava.

'So – you're really not going to see him again, over Mario Kart?' asks Bethan. Ravi puts his arm around her in the unconscious way Billie often sees couples do in order to physically reinforce their partnership when commiserating with their single friends. She imagines Bethan and Ravi whispering about her grief later, in the calm dark of the moments before they fall asleep, treating it as one of the day's pieces of business they might pass a closing comment on. It's an unfair image of them and Billie feels ashamed for having imagined it.

'It just gave me the ick,' says Laura. Billie watches her search for some more evidence to support her position.

'Chicken rating?' Bethan asks Angus, pointing at his plate.

'Oh, ten out of ten, easily,' he says and gives her a double thumbs-up.

Angus had an Instagram account where he uploaded reviews of chicken nuggets called The Nug Life Chose Me that had fewer than 100 followers and which Billie recently noticed has been quietly phased out. The memory of it causes a wrench of sadness that takes her by surprise. Laura straightens up in her chair again.

'And that wasn't the only thing. In the morning, I was doing my moisturiser in the toilet mirror and he was like, "Can I come in and pee?" and I was like,' she scrunches up her face, '"no", so he went off and had a shower and then later when we were out having brunch I noticed he never went to pee so I asked him why not and he said he just peed in the shower.'

Laura holds an appalled expression. Billie thinks of this poor man being quizzed on the fullness of his bladder over huevos rancheros, which dredges up a smile.

They all catch each other's eyes, and Laura notices.

'What now?'

'You don't pee in the shower?' Angus says carefully.

'Of course I don't pee in the shower, Angus. That's disgusting.'

'Laura, everybody pees in the shower,' says Ravi, laughing. 'How is that something you don't know?'

Laura takes a moment to process this.

'No they don't,' she says briskly.

Her eyes widen and she turns to Bethan and then to Billie.

'You pee in our shower?'

Billie nods.

'All the time,' Bethan says, making motions to stand and clear some plates. At this, Angus jumps out of his chair and begins loading his arms with crockery and moving clumsily around the tight space of the kitchen to set himself up at the sink. Bethan sits back down again heavily and smiles a thank you.

'Well, I think that's barbaric,' Laura says.

'He's got a separate bathroom and toilet though,' says Angus, turning back from the sink towards them with an impressed face. 'Gotta count for something.'

Angus smiles, enjoying his quip. Billie finds it irritating because she has long suspected that he is only playing at renting before his parents buy him a place to live, and that such a place will unquestionably have a separate bathroom and toilet. She watches him doing the dishes, and notices that he is diligently scrubbing the plates with cold water and no Fairy liquid.

Laura, fed up of being disagreed with, is no longer paying attention to any of them and is on her phone instead. Lately she has been trying to fix a problem with her posture she refers to as her 'text neck' by holding her phone right up at eye level when she uses it, which makes it look like she's constantly filming things to report them to the police.

Ravi picks up one of the architectural-looking potatoes from the sideboard that did not make it into their dinner. 'I don't really get it,' he says, holding it up and turning it over in his fingers. 'What's the point of them being a special shape? What's it called again? Tourniquet?'

'Tournée,' says Bethan. She looks exhausted but content. She puts her head on his shoulder. 'I don't know. But I get in trouble if they're not all exactly like that one.'

'I think they're beautiful,' he says, bopping her gently on the forehead with it.

'Shall we sit soft for pudding?' says Angus in a parodically plummy voice, having finished his approximation of washing up. They contort themselves out of their chairs, hemmed

104

in close on each side by the various white goods, and move towards the living room. Here, they have two tired, leather-look sofas that make damp creaking noises for a long time after you stand up from them, once a uniform beige and now bruised by the transfer of years' worth of dye from previous tenants' jeans. Billie doubles back, remembering that the dessert was her responsibility, although it had been obvious that Bethan only asked her to do it to keep her occupied. She works her fingers into the seal of their greying fridge door to jemmy it open, and retrieves five mismatched glasses with chocolate mousse and a blotch of collapsed whipped cream in them. She rams a teaspoon into each one, feeling a dull satisfaction at ruining their appearance, and brings them in on a chopping board. The four of them coo and clap as she enters the living room.

'These look fantastic, Billie,' says Angus, a great smile of encouragement on his face.

'It's all Bethan. I'm just the lackey.'

She sits down beside Laura on one of the sofas, Bethan and Ravi on the one opposite. Angus relaxes into a beanbag, his knees crabbed out to each side.

'So you're off to Paris in the morning, then?' Angus asks in a gentle voice, which reminds Billie of the way people speak to small children.

'Yeah. Going to stay with Tom for a few days. The funeral won't be for a bit anyway because they need to – it takes time to repatriate a body. Apparently.'

Four sincere faces nod at her.

'Right, of course. Well, that's great, that you're going,' Angus says. 'Good to stay busy.'

'Yeah, definitely good to be distracted,' Ravi adds. She doesn't know where he is drawing this expertise from, but she nods anyway.

'If he's a prick you'll come home though, yeah? Don't—' Bethan looks for words, worry creasing her forehead. 'I don't know. I just hope he's going to look after you properly, that's all.'

Billie looks deep into her mousse. In truth, Bethan hardly knows Tom. What she does know of him is all received knowledge from Billie, so she feels a sort proxy guilt to hear Bethan describe him in these terms, even as it is nice to hear someone take her side. It's support, but support ultimately of her own manufacturing.

As Ravi takes a large mouthful of dessert, his eyes bulge and he makes a noise garbled by mousse. He swallows hastily.

'Oh my God,' he says, slamming a palm against his chest to aid the passage of food, 'I can't believe I haven't told you yet about the chocolate.'

'What chocolate?' says Bethan, giving Ravi a half-hearted pat on the back as he coughs.

'The builder, you know the builder at my—' he starts saying to Bethan and then realises he needs to start from the beginning for the benefit of the others. He shakes his hands in the air to rewind.

'Okay, so, my parents are having the bathroom redone,' he begins.

'Oh shit yeah, how is he?' Bethan interrupts, but Ravi waves her down.

'Right yeah, so they have these builders in at the moment, three of them. Nice guys. And I came back to the house yesterday, and there was only one of them and he seemed really rattled. So I asked him what was wrong and he said one of the other guys, older guy called Alex, he'd collapsed. They heard the sound of him thudding to the ground upstairs in the bathroom, went up there and they couldn't wake him up, he was out cold and his eyes were going all like—' Ravi shakes his two first fingers back and forth, 'and he'd pissed himself.'

'Oh Jesus,' says Angus obligingly.

'And so they called an ambulance and they didn't know what was wrong with him at the hospital, he was just totally unresponsive.'

Laura makes a face somewhere between concern and boredom.

'Anyway I was like, oh man that's awful. And then, you know, didn't think too much about it. But today I was looking for my watch and so I opened the drawer by my bed, and I had a couple of bars of magic mushroom chocolate in there,' he says, and then pre-empts Bethan's disapproval, 'from ages ago, last summer or something.'

Billie sees where the story is going and allows herself to disengage a little. Angus has caught on too and gives a quick, loud laugh.

'Except there weren't two bars of chocolate, there was one. And I'm looking at it and thinking . . . there were definitely two bars here. And then suddenly I was like, oh fuck. So I went to find the other guy and said to him, is there any way Alex maybe ate some chocolate out of my room. And he was like, no no, don't think so. But then I explained why I was asking and then immediately he was like, okay yes, he came

107

in and said he'd found chocolate and offered us all a piece, and we told him not to eat it but I guess maybe he did.'

Ravi shakes his head in a terror tinged with respect.

'So this guy accidentally ate about eight doses of magic mushrooms in one go.'

'Holy shit,' says Angus.

'Oh my God, that's horrible,' says Laura, aghast.

Bethan makes a small noise of disgust.

'You shouldn't just keep – you need to throw that stuff away, Jesus,' she says.

Ravi nods at her in a placating way.

'Isn't that insane? Apparently the guy who took him to the hospital was convinced he was already dead. Crying his eyes out, really going through it, being like, oh my God, Alex is dead, Alex is dead—'

Taking a spoonful of dessert, Billie bites her tongue. It sends a bolt of pain through the centre of her head and she flinches hard. Bethan squeezes Ravi's arm.

'Maybe we save the rest of this story for another time,' she says.

Billie realises what her shudder has been misinterpreted as and thinks about trying to correct them. Then she doesn't. She had not been finding this acknowledgement of the existence of death upsetting, and now feels alienated by the fact that she had not even made the link. She is hit without warning by a heavy need to be alone. Ravi looks at her, and a brief horror lights his eyes and then dims again.

'Oh. Sure, no bother.'

There is a blunt silence. Then, Laura claps her hands, making Bethan jump a little.

'Right, Angus, I think it's hometime.'

Angus nods sagely, as though this is what he had been about to say. Billie sees Ravi and Bethan having a swift, mute conversation of brow twitching and eye widening in her peripheral vision. She eases herself up from the sofa as it parps and putters in her wake, and moves towards the kitchen.

'I can clean up,' Laura says, 'you should sleep.'

Billie feels a wave of gratitude for Laura.

'Just this once though, next time everyone has to stay to help,' Laura adds, and the wave recedes.

Angus shrugs his zip-up jacket on and they all shuffle themselves through some goodbyes. Ravi and Bethan each give long, meaningful hugs to Billie and retire to bed. Billie trudges around the small space of her bedroom, collecting things like passport and hairbrush to add to her bag, which she notices now contains an almost random assortment of her belongings.

She lies in bed feeling small and blank for a while. Then she runs her tongue over her teeth and gets up again. Out in the narrow corridor, she finds Ravi, on his way out of the bathroom. He gives her a polite smile and moves towards Bethan's room.

'What happened to the builder? To Alex,' Billie asks in a low voice.

Ravi turns back.

'Oh yeah, he's fine. Mostly fine.'

Ravi shifts his stance in a way that makes Billie think he's only now aware that he's wearing boxers and nothing else.

'Apparently he has these recurring nightmares where he's being zipped into a body bag.'

Billie nods for lack of another response.

'Night, Ravi.'

She goes into the bathroom, where she brushes her teeth, behind and around and across each surface, as she considers her father's corpse for the first time.

9

Billie watches as Tom leaves the flat in a flurry of backpack stuffing and snatched bites from the now very solid piece of baguette. No one was free to cover his shift in the evening, but he's persuaded someone to swap him for a daytime one. She lies in bed for as long as she can bear before she needs to pee. On the toilet, staring at a scab of disintegrating plaster on the wall, she thinks about what she's going to do with her day before Tom gets back. She knows that staying here in the flat is too tragic, but she doesn't feel like doing anything else.

Back in the room, she sits on Tom's bed to feel out the edges of her hangover. It's bad, but not quite bad enough to be an excuse to stay in bed all day. She has an aftertaste of embarrassment, although she can't remember anything specific she said or did to be embarrassed about, and has to remind herself that the only person to be embarrassed in front of was her own brother.

She watches three episodes of a TV show she doesn't

especially like, and then reaches for her phone to call her mum. It rings briefly before a voice that isn't quite her mum's answers.

'Bill! Hello.'

'Oh, hey.'

'She left her phone in here – she's just back from church, hold on. Can you switch it to video?'

Helen has always called her Bill. Apparently she'd found it funny, when Billie had been a toddler with big eyes and ringlets, to announce to the room that 'the Old Bill' was here whenever she waddled in. Billie hangs up and calls back with video. Helen's face appears, all glasses and nose, looking at her phone screen with a pained expression.

'How are you doing?'

'Fine,' Billie says, 'thanks. Nice glasses.'

Helen beams, touching the green frames. Last time Billie had seen her, at Christmas, she had been making do with a pair that had to be fastened round the back of her head with an elastic band.

'Thank you very much. Shall I go and get her?'

Billie watches the ceilings change above Helen's forehead.

'Actually, wait – wait for a second,' she says.

Helen puts her face back in front of the camera as she walks. The dog barks in the background.

'Mmm?'

'How is she?'

Helen stops moving briefly.

'Hold on, just a second.'

She changes course into another room. Billie hears the door close behind her.

'How's your mum?' Helen says.

'Yeah.'

She hears Helen brush a pile of items aside, some of them thudding to the floor, and sees her flop down onto the sofa.

'Well . . . she's okay,' she says in a discreet voice. 'Yes, she's all right.'

'Okay.'

'But are *you* all right, chicken?'

'I guess,' Billie says, picking at the bobbles on Tom's duvet cover. 'I just wanted to ask because . . . yeah, she doesn't always want to say how she is, to me, I think. Like, how she actually is.'

Helen sighs.

'Well, she's okay. It's been a bit of a shock of course, but you know. And she's safe and sound here with me. You don't have to worry about her.'

'Yeah, but that's the thing isn't it, I worry anyway, so I might as well know how she really is.'

Helen considers this for a few moments.

'She's a tough nut to crack, your mum. Always has been. Lots of space for other people's feelings, but not much space for her own, that sort of thing.'

Billie murmurs in agreement.

'But does she like, talk to you? About stuff?'

'She does now, yes.'

'Okay.'

'She hasn't always, but yes, we've been talking. And that's not all her fault, that we didn't before, as much. It's mine too.'

'Yeah.'

113

Her aunt looks at her for a moment, her head slightly inclined to the side.

'And who are you talking to?'

Billie looks at her own face in its tiny square icon as she thinks.

'My friends, a bit. Tom, sort of. I dunno.'

'Is Tom there?'

'No, he's at work.'

'Right, okay.'

Martha barks again while neither of them speaks.

'Well, give him my love,' Helen says. 'And you know you can talk to me. Boring and old as I may be.'

Billie forces an exhalation of breath to seem like she's laughing.

'Thank you.'

'So: Mum, let me get her.' Helen makes a series of middle-aged noises as she rises.

'Actually, I'll call her again later, I'm in a bit of a rush now.'

'Sure, okay. All right, well, take care, will you?'

'Yep,' says Billie, doing a pursed-lip smile and nodding.

'Bye now.'

'Bye.'

Billie hangs up and looks at the wall. She doesn't speak to people about her family in any detail. And she doesn't speak to Tom about anything, really. She thinks about calling Bethan but the thought of talking about any of this makes her feel trapped behind her own teeth.

She starts to read and respond to some of the messages from friends who are thinking of her at 'this difficult time'. The number of texts suggests that Bethan has been in touch now with more or less everybody who Billie would want to know the news. She feels relieved not to have to spread the word herself. There is one from Angus.

> Hey, I hope you don't mind me texting. I wasn't sure if it would be intruding to say so in person the other night, but I just wanted to say I'm really thinking of you, and hope you're doing as okay as can be expected.

The accurate punctuation and careful phrasing tells Billie that he redrafted it a number of times. Bethan has sent her a photo of her latest work-related burn, a forearm with a seething red welt across it, to which Billie replies 'nice'. There is also a message from Angus's mother. She deletes it without reading it, but the idea of its existence annoys her enough not to want to respond to Angus, which annoys her further because it makes her suspect that she is a bad person even more so than she usually does when interacting with him. Angus's flawless conduct does not reflect well on her. If their positions had been reversed, there is no way she would be as kind and forgiving as Angus has been, and this knowledge is unpalatable. Bethan sends another message.

> Everything going okay?

Billie strains to think for a moment and then sends a thumbs-up back.

Tom has steadied one of the legs of his table with a yellowing Dorling Kindersley guide from the late noughties. She replaces it with one of the French novels from his shelf and then sits at the table flicking through the guidebook while eating a bowl of stale chocolate cereal, and then another. The book tells her that the best views of Paris are not, in fact, from the Eiffel Tower, but from an anonymous-looking skyscraper on the other side of the river. She decides to go to the Eiffel Tower anyway, because it feels soothing in its obviousness. She puts some make-up on, leaning forward over a curved shard of mirror resting against the wall by Tom's sink like some kind of primitive hunting tool. In the shard, she gradually begins to see the face of a person fit to mix in human society. She gathers up her things to leave.

The woman at the opposite side of the bar is feeding her dog the charcuterie board she ordered, slice by slice. Tom is trying to do the maths in his head of how much each of these slices of charcuterie costs. The whole board, including salami, parma ham, a slightly plasticky chorizo and a few grey gherkins, comes to seventeen euros. He has learnt to pass the time in this way, little moments of mental exercise to remind himself that he is alive. He counted all the glasses in his line of vision once, made as many words as he could using the letters in the word *pharmacie*, visible in a sickly green out of the window and across the street. Chimera, impeach, apache. This one's too tricky, though, as the items he needs to count keep disappearing down the throat of a Pomeranian.

He looks at his phone for somewhere to put his eyes. To his surprise, he has received an email in the two minutes since he last checked it. It's a Google alert summary for Nour's name. These come in occasionally, usually about another

Nour Choukri who is a newspaper photographer in Leipzig. But today, finally, it's his Nour. He clicks the link in the email, aware of a faint ringing in his ears. It brings up a sparse, sharply designed website for a literary magazine, and a story with her name at the top.

He stands behind the bar reading the story and remembering to breathe. He doesn't bother to look up words he doesn't know, chasing through the sentences as quickly as he can. He isn't sure how much time has passed when he reaches the end. He looks up and blinks into the sunlight that has begun to shine into the pub without him noticing. A small woman is standing in front of him in silence, smiling and waiting to be served.

'*Pardon*,' he says, and takes her order for an IPA. He tries to return to himself. The woman takes her beer, and Noémie tramps down the stairs and joins him behind the bar.

'I'm bored,' she announces, looking at him expectantly. 'Now what?'

'Me too,' he says in someone else's voice. He has an idea, and doesn't have the energy to interrogate whether it's a good one.

'Could you read something for me? In French.'

'Yes, okay,' she says, looking unexcited by this prospect. 'One second.'

Tom picks his phone back up from under the bar, navigates to the story and hands the phone to Noémie. She looks at the screen and raises her eyebrows a little.

'I just want to know what you think. If it's good.'

'Don't be that creepy guy, the ex-boyfriend always checking her business,' she says, shaking her head.

'No, yeah. I'm only curious because she was really excited about getting published.'

Noémie purses her lips.

'I'm not stalking her! I'm not, could you – look, will you read it or not?'

'Is it long?'

'No.'

'Okay yes, I will. This time.'

She leans forward on the bar and settles to read. Tom instinctively takes a can of craft beer out of the fridge, and is on the verge of opening it before he remembers he's not drinking and puts it back. Noémie fiddles with her eyebrow bar as she scrolls. He can't stand still.

'I'm going to smoke,' says Tom, although the idea of a cigarette at this moment makes him feel ill.

'No, do the sauces, then you smoke,' she says, eyes still on his phone.

'Fine.'

Doing the sauces is Tom's least favourite job in the pub. The senior manager does not allow them to put out half-empty bottles of ketchup, mayonnaise, mustard and barbecue sauce on the tables, but he also does not allow them to throw out the half-empty bottles. Instead, they have to save the dregs of each bottle and add them to a congealing vat of what the pub advertises on the menu as its 'sauce maison'. It is the colour of earwax. But by the time Tom has finished the scraping and smearing, Noémie has put his phone down.

'What did you think?' he asks.

'It's okay.'

'Just okay.' Tom feels too warm.

118

'I don't know. I don't know about literature and this stuff,' Noémie says, shrugging.

Tom nods, thinking that he should have anticipated a nothing-y response. Noémie and Nour had never quite clicked.

'It's kind of . . . ' Noémie adds, wrinkling her nose, 'I don't know. For me, I am bored of reading about men who are like that.'

'Like what?'

He watches her rifle through a mental library of terms that he wishes he could see, a panicked adrenaline racing across his shoulders.

'Monsters,' she says.

The walk to the Eiffel Tower takes Billie an hour. She would have liked it to be longer. Walking gives her body a rhythm that keeps her thoughts in check. She walks mostly beside the river, its flow anchoring her with another predictable forward movement. Twice, she stops to buy a croissant, chasing the small waves of pleasure that subside even before she has swallowed each bite. On the walk, Billie makes up her mind that she will take the stairs up the tower, in the hope that either physical exertion or a sense of achievement will provide enough endorphins on which to ride out the rest of the day. In the long queue to begin the climb, a man in a pair of sunglasses on a string who is holding the same Dorling Kindersley guide as she is catches her eye. He smiles and nods at her, holding his book a little higher in recognition. Billie pretends she hasn't seen him.

She begins the climb, looking down at her feet and the patches of worn metal cross hatch beneath them. The sound of her steps is calming, and she tries to enter the peace of the tempo and use it to think about the funeral. She had intended to use the plane journey, the forced exile from the internet, to decide what she was going to say. She had typed three words into her Notes app: 'my dad was' and felt instantly drained. She looked out of the window for the rest of the flight with her headphones in but nothing playing, listening to the plugged-up sound of her own internal fluids and the plane engines beyond. Now, as she tries to produce some ideas, the futility of the exercise smacks her in the face again.

Billie is one third of the way up the tower when she decides that this was a stupid and bad idea, and that she's too tired to walk any more. She sits down on one of the steps, which bites her with unexpected cold, and looks out beyond the beige grating at the view. It spreads out impressively, even at this height. Billie thinks about the fact that there is only one person in the whole of the city who knows who she is. It becomes hard to imagine standing up again. Then her stomach flashes with anxious nausea as she thinks of the woman she hit with her suitcase who, in fairness, would probably also recognise her.

The sounds of clanking steps and laughter from below tell her that turning back around would be a humiliation to her and a hazard to others, so she forces her legs to carry her to the top of this flight of stairs, muscles screaming and her breath high up in her throat. From there, she takes the lift to the very top of the tower, pressed into the bodies of strangers as her insides swoop.

At the highest observation deck, there is a huge, muscular man lying face down on the floor, his meaty fingers searching for grip on the linoleum. Next to him, a little girl gently instructs him to stop it, squatting down to pat his shoulder, and a woman in a lanyard gestures for people to stay back.

'We can go down now, monsieur,' the woman says, 'but you must walk.'

The man shakes his head hard, and spreads his limbs out even further to put as much of his body surface in contact with the floor as possible. The rest of the people on the observation deck have all subtly stopped looking out at the city and have started to watch him.

'You can . . . ' the woman struggles and haltingly begins to mime, putting her hands out in front of her one after the other like she's playing the bongos, but the man is still face down and can't see her.

'Crawl,' Billie offers, and the woman glances at her gratefully.

'Crawl, yes, monsieur, to the elevator.'

The little girl gets down and begins to demonstrate for her dad. He flexes an arm and a leg in an attempt to move, and then is defeated again and starts sobbing.

'It's moving, it's not safe,' the man cries, as the woman with the lanyard calls for reinforcements on a walkie talkie. Billie and the other visitors pretend that the act of taking in the view has rendered them deaf to the small wails coming from the floor.

Eventually, four people in lanyards roll the man over and begin to hoist him up by his limbs. The obvious effort this involves attracts a couple of the larger bystanders to assist, and they begin lumbering him towards the service lift like a battering ram. The little girl follows them, strangely unexcited about the commotion. Once the lift doors close to ferry the man away, an awkward calm descends on the deck, as though the people there are now participating in an uncomfortable silence instead of simply being strangers to each other.

Now that the man has planted the idea in her mind, Billie can't shake the feeling that perhaps he is right. She looks out over the rooftops and stands very still. She can't decide whether the tower really is lilting slightly in the wind, or whether it's the same feeling she's had for days now, that she is on the verge of falling from a great height.

10

The house is quiet this weekend because Billie is away on a school trip. It's the same one Tom went on four years ago, a couple of hours from their school on the coach, and you get to stay overnight for three days and do outdoor activities. Tom thinks she's being a coward about the trip. She called their mum from the phone by the showers on Friday morning, when she hadn't even been there a whole day, and he could hear Billie moaning on the other end of the line, saying that if they made her go on the big zip-wire at the end of the trip she would have a stroke and die. Tom knows that Billie doesn't know what strokes are. She saw the advert on the television where they explained that if someone's face goes droopy and they can't speak, you should call the ambulance. After they saw the advert together, Tom thought about pretending to have a stroke to see if she'd been listening properly and would try to save his life, but it wasn't convincing enough when he practised doing half a dead face in the mirror.

Tom hasn't been at home this long without Billie since

she was born. This Sunday will be the first Sunday he can remember going to church without her, which will be strange even though he is always careful not to be seen talking to Billie much at church, because she's small and stupid and this lowers his standing with the other boys. Last week, he said he had a stomach ache, so Billie and their mum went without him and he stayed in his bedroom until they came back. He said a prayer in case he was in trouble for not going, but only a short one because he's pretty sure God doesn't care about the things he does, one way or another. But the stomach ache lie won't work two weeks in a row. His need for a longer-term way out of church is becoming urgent.

Having lain awake most of the night worrying about it, he woke up this morning with a clear and good idea at the front of his mind. Just because he goes to church, doesn't mean he has to go to the Sunday school. In fact, when he goes down to collect some breakfast and asks his mum whether he can sit with her in the main bit of the church today, she seems happy about it. The real service is more boring than Sunday school, and truthfully even being in the building makes him feel ill now, but staying with the adults rather than going upstairs will be an improvement. He waits in his room until he hears the rattle of the car keys, then runs down and out to the car, because while he was eating his toast he could tell the air wasn't right in the house, and he should keep himself to himself.

His mum is quiet on the drive and she turns the radio up loud to try to hide it. She is her home-self in the car as well as in the house, he has noticed. When they arrive at church, that person stays in the car, and she becomes the other version of his mum, cheery and interested. Tom stays close beside her and takes a sweep of their surroundings outside the huge arch of the front door. Neither of them are here. Maybe they aren't coming this week.

Inside the church, his mum moves through the people, saying hello, pressing Tom on the shoulder to do the same. She has the same conversation with everybody, and Tom's eyes pass between the pews. No sign of Owen or Ryan, or any of their parents. His stomach unclenches a little, and he gives the verger with a brown tooth a polite smile.

The service today doesn't include any of the hymns that Tom likes best. No thumping opening notes to *How Great Thou Art*, not the calm melody of *Lord of All Hopefulness*, not the unanswered question 'O who am I?' in *My Song is Love Unknown* that turns Tom's heart over and makes him feel a nice kind of pain he doesn't really understand. He mumbles his way through *Thine Be The Glory* listening to his mum's voice, which sits on top of the general noise, carefully getting all the notes right. He zones out for the readings, too distracted by how mature he must be appearing to everyone, sat down here away from the children.

When it is finally finished, Tom and his mum hang around outside. He watches as the Sunday school clatters down the stairs and each child goes to meet their parents, and he gives various people he knows a grown-up nod of greeting. His mum always wants to talk to everyone, and today it seems to take even longer than usual. He goes to stand beside her, to imply by his hovering that he wants to leave, and to his horror he sees that she is talking to Owen's mum, and that they are here after all. He whips around, his eyes wild, and comes face to face with Owen himself.

'Hello, Tom Perrin,' Owen says with an unreadable look on his face.

Tom says hello back. The adulthood of the previous hour escapes him and he feels an old urge to take his mum's hand. He turns his face away from Owen and pretends to be interested in what their mothers are saying to each other. He waits for the crawling seconds to pass, feeling unbearably present in his body. When Owen's mum finally announces that they are leaving, Tom says a silent thank you to someone, anyone. Owen turns back as they walk away to smirk at him, and Tom's panic turns into resolve. He has one week to work out how he will never come back here.

They are almost the last people standing outside the church once everyone else has wandered away to do whatever it is that other families do on Sundays. He wonders whether he and his mum will go home now, and his nerves jangle again. They walk back to the car slowly, and Tom tries and fails to read the way she's walking for signs of what will happen next. As they shut the car doors and his mum goes back to her quiet self, Tom waits for the verdict.

'How hungry are you?' she asks. He doesn't know what answer to give, what outcome it will produce.

'Not that hungry. A little hungry.'

'What about lunch in the pub, as a treat? With the football?' she says, a brighter sound in her voice.

Tom says yes please. Football games are easily two hours with half -time and stoppage. He doesn't actually like football that much, but his mum has been an Arsenal fan her whole life. He understands that it is his job as a boy to inherit this from her, even if he has managed to dodge all her attempts to get him to take an interest in playing football himself.

The pub is dark and smells funny but they do a roast on Sundays, and Tom has a feeling his mum will let him get chips on the side even though you get mashed potato included. They are lucky to find a table in the room full of men and their sons in red shirts. Tom thinks this good luck could bode well for the rest of the day. The first goal comes right after their food arrives, and in the uproar of people jumping and holding each other, he has a flash of inspiration. He waits until half-time, working his way through the slab of beef to calm his jitters. When the whistle goes, his stomach plunges.

'Mum?'

'Yes, my love,' she stays, still looking contemplatively at the screen.

'Did you know Sean plays football on Sundays?'

She turns to her own portion of chips, mostly uneaten so far, and puts one in the ketchup. They must be cold.

'Mmmhmm,' she says, and puts the chip in her mouth.

'I think maybe I want to do football with him,' he says.

'Oh!' She looks pleased and Tom feels a trickle of guilt. 'Well, sure, great. Why the change of heart?'

'Sean says it's fun.'

'Okay. Great, I'll get the details from Sinéad.'

'It's in the morning,' Tom says, 'on Sundays.'

His mum looks at him, a nothing kind of expression on her face.

'So I wouldn't be able to do church any more,' he says, to make sure she's understood.

She nods lightly, and he can't read her thoughts.

'Okay,' she says at last. 'If that's what you want. You're old enough to decide for yourself now, my love.'

Tom floods with relief, but it's mixed in with something like dread that he hadn't expected.

'Thanks.'

She gives him a small smile. Tom makes a mental note to improve significantly at football in the next seven days, and acknowledges to himself that it is quite likely he will get kicked in the head by one of Sean's heavy-set and scary brothers.

Arsenal beat Reading two-nil, with goals from Touré and Fàbregas, but his mum only claps in a muted way when the match is finished. The crowd watching the television all turn away from it at once, and go back to being just people. Tom watches her face. Her thoughts are still a mystery to him. He eats her chips and she doesn't say anything about it.

Eventually his mum makes movements to leave, and Tom follows her. When they're in the car again, as he pulls his seat-belt across him, she suggests they go to the park. He agrees, although he's tired out by the day and there are dark clouds beginning to gather above them. On the drive, Tom tries to invite his mum into a discussion of the game, the unfair yellow card, the controversial line call, but he can't get her to contribute much.

As the wheels hit the gravel of the carpark, the clouds open and heavy rain begins to spit down on the windshield. Tom's heart sinks. They come to a stop in a parking space. He and his mum both peer up and out at the sky, a low grey sheet that stretches to the buildings in all directions. He hears her let all the air out of her lungs.

They listen to the rain for a while, the hammering droplets reminding Tom that the car is a sealed metal box. He wonders if it is raining like this where Billie is. He wonders if the zip-wire will be cancelled.

'Okay. Let's go home,' his mum says.

The rain continues to fall. He can see his mum's hands, small and white, holding the steering wheel. She doesn't move. Tom follows the path of one raindrop, slithering down the window beside him, gathering speed and size as it races towards the bottom to vanish into the rest of the water settled there. He does this with several more raindrops, top to bottom, top to bottom, before he feels the car's engine finally rumbling beneath him.

11

The shower is only just big enough to accommodate them both. Angus goes in first, squashing himself into one of the far corners and raising both arms above his head. Then Billie follows, sliding the door behind her with a hand pressed flat against the glass as she reaches up to detach the shower head from its bracket on the wall. The water is freezing for the first minute, so she pushes herself against him and sprays the nozzle away from them, cold slicing at the undersides of their feet, until it is warm. She holds the shower head with one hand and uses the other to bring the body wash to her mouth where she can prise the cap off with her teeth. The chemical taste as she runs her tongue across the residue on her lips makes the coconut smell feel like a lie. She squirts the soap directly down his chest, and then begins lathering it against his surfaces and angles. It is unfortunate that this action, the warm, wet stroking of his body, has become un-sexualised for both of them. When she reaches up to wash his neck and the backs of his ears, he gives her a goofy, lopsided look of apology. She asks him to spin around, which produces some low, rude squeaks of foot on acrylic, and he continues to keep his hands aloft, as though for a firing squad. The wetter the bin-bags taped around his hands get, the more they cling to his fingers, and she can see that they're curled forward like the claws of some very tall, hairless animal. After she rinses him off, he gives her a kiss on the top of her head and edges out of the shower so she can wash herself. Through the fogged glass she can see him standing there on the bathmat, naked and dripping, waiting placidly until she is ready to towel him.

It has been like this for a month now. The casts are due to come off in one week, at which point Angus has plans to embark on what he is calling a night out 'to end all nights out'. This seems unwise to Billie, given that his last night out had in fact ended their nights out. She had stepped outside for a cigarette at the house party in time to watch him climb from a grimy garden table onto one of his friend's shoulders, who was in turn sitting on the shoulders of some other guy. All three of them were roaring incoherently. As the person at the bottom began trying to stand up and complete the human tower, shuddering with his inability to admit that he wasn't strong enough to do it, Billie foresaw the coming events. He would pitch forward, tipping the other two with him, onto the concrete patio, or else the garden wall. She heard the voices of some other bystanders try to stop them, and by the time she had decided to override her instinct not to be the nagging girlfriend and intervene, it was already happening. Angus threw out both his hands to absorb the fall, and she wasn't sure whether the cracking noises had been the sounds of his wrists breaking or made by one of the dozens of empty cans of lager littering the ground. It was lucky, really, that he had been so drunk, because he didn't seem to be in any pain, and had allowed Billie to lead him away from the party and into the ambulance, doddering with contentment like an aged dignitary leaving a gala. The paramedics gave him gas and air and as they drove to the hospital he kept telling her how silly he was and trying to reach out and touch her with his mangled hands.

His parents had descended on the hospital, sweeping a cold waft of perfume and wax jackets in with them, and thanked Billie for being so good. Once both of his arms were encased in bubblegum pink casts, they swaddled him up as much as it is possible to swaddle up a twenty-year-old man of six foot four, and took him home to Cambridgeshire for a week. Here, Billie knew he could expect to be pampered to within an inch of his life by various people in the employ of his family. Angus lives in a house that is so big part of it needs to be open to the public. One of his favourite stories to roll out for new company involves a tour group interrupting him during a bath. But after a week of watching television and being climbed all over by his spaniels, he had grown bored and decided to return to their student house in south London. He had called Billie to check that she would be okay to look after him, given the state he was in. Of course, she'd said, because she did want to look after him. She thinks now, though, both that she had not appreciated what this would involve and that his parents should have done some of that appreciating for them and kept him at home. He is now capable of wiping his own arse, but even that took some initial teamwork to figure out.

Her friends sympathise with her and say that it must be

annoying, and she feels that perhaps she ought to be more annoyed. Partly, it's that Angus is a difficult person to stay annoyed with. He thanks her constantly, and buys her little presents to show that he understands what an inconvenience this all is, presents she has to pay for with his card by rooting around in his jeans pockets at the till while he holds his arms out above her head like he's riding a motorcycle with two broken arms, which is only marginally more reckless than something Angus would actually do. He has large, deep eyes beneath endearingly sloped eyebrows that make him look a little worried all the time. And more than anything else, he has a good heart, and has chosen to give it to her, a fact which puts an upper limit on her capacity to be irritated at having to manoeuvre his shirts onto him like he's a shop mannequin. She finds that, on some level, she enjoys it, seeing so many needs and being able to fulfil them, but something about that enjoyment does not seem to fit with how other people regard her situation, and it bothers her. Maybe it's just that they've not yet been together for a year, and the window of not being annoyed will close in the near future. She doesn't know, having never had a boyfriend before. She likes Angus very much. The thrilling early part of their relationship, when she had hummed with unbearable anticipation waiting to meet him outside the library, seemed to pass very quickly, though. Now, when he comes into a room, she finds herself silently asking: am I happy to see you? How happy is happy enough?

Today, they are going to meet his parents at Somerset House for the annual Redmond family ice skating trip. This is one of many things that the Redmonds do every year in the same way. The second weekend in December is for ice skating, specifically at Somerset House, and is 'a non-negotiable occasion', although it doesn't seem like Angus would want to get out of it even if he could. Angus and his family adore each other. Not even his brother Alfie seems to bring down the total quantity of enjoyment they get out of each other's company. Alfie is a sour, squatter version of Angus who's doing a PhD in 'foam', about which he won't give much more detail other than to say that foam has the same structure as the universe, which Billie doesn't find elucidates things much. The Redmonds think the contrast between Alfie and Angus is hilarious. They are always pulling the elder brother into begrudged hugs and poking him for reactions, to which Alfie is always surly but nothing more sinister. Alfie's girlfriend Elle will also be coming, an accomplished university gymnast who is very good at finding ways to wedge the fact that she is tiny into conversation.

Angus won't be able to participate in the skating because of his wrists. As far as she knows, Billie can't skate. These two facts together do not absolve them from their duty to go, apparently, but she understands that this is an integral part of being the girlfriend of someone like Angus. She sees his parents frequently. They come to London a lot, and when they do they take Angus and Billie out for long and luxurious lunches. They are very nice to her, and she tries to believe Angus when he says that these lunches are not a big deal to them, and she doesn't need to ask before ordering whether the price of the thing she's ordering is okay. They always ask after her own parents, whom they've never met, and are politely unprobing about whatever answer she gives them. Her dad having a new girlfriend is wonderful. The fact that her mum now suddenly lives in Scotland with her sister is lovely, and an occasion for them to talk about their last trip to Gleneagles, which Billie finds out is a famous hotel from googling it in the toilets.

They meet inside the courtyard. Angus's dad, George, is wrapped up in a mustard scarf. He has the kind of ears and nose that remind Billie of the fact that your ears and nose never stop growing, and they are already red from the cold. Olivia, Angus's mother, is dressed like the dowager queen of a now-defunct Soviet state, and Alfie is making fun of their fellow skaters in a quiet undertone to Elle, who is being tiny. They all greet each other, with a variety of cheek kisses for the girls and back-slapping hugs for the boys. Billie and Elle give each other the customary smile that says, 'I, too, am a girlfriend.'

'Gosh, darling, don't you look healthy! Lots of lovely mince pies, I suspect,' Olivia says, giving Billie a brilliant smile and squeezing her shoulder hard.

Billie confesses that she forgot to bring gloves.

'Oh, have my muff,' Olivia says, to the uproarious and prolonged laughter of Angus and his dad, and a series of tinkling giggles from Elle. Billie takes the muff from her, and does her widest smile. It's warm in her hands and very soft, like a rabbit that hasn't quite finished dying.

They go to trade their shoes in for skates, and sit in a makeshift tent bent over themselves to put them on. Beside Billie, a glove curled up into the 'OK' gesture is lying on the pocked flooring.

'Now be careful of this one,' George tells Billie, pointing at his wife, 'she's a real speed demon out there.'

135

Olivia waggles her eyebrows mischievously as she yanks her laces tighter. George tells Billie, primarily, because it seems the rest of them have all heard it before, about how he and his wife have friends with a private rink on their estate because one of their sons had become obsessed with ice hockey, and that the adults used to race around it once the children were in bed. The loser of each race would have to remove an item of clothing. All the Redmonds except Alfie laugh, beaming joy into each other's faces, unbothered by this acknowledgment of their all having bodies that could be naked.

'Such fun we have up there,' says George, patting his wife's knee emphatically.

'Tell them about the bicycle game,' Angus goads them, turning to Billie with a 'you'll like this' expression. Olivia groans a performed embarrassment.

'Oh lord, now no doubt you'll think this terribly irresponsible,' George says to Billie and Elle. He goes on to describe a game in which they would split into pairs, one with a bicycle and one with a disassembled rifle. They would drink heavily with lunch, then go out onto a field where the person with the bicycle had to cycle away as fast as possible while the person with the gun put it together and tried to shoot the receding target of their partner's back.

'Only air rifles, of course,' George adds once he has finished laughing expansively, the laughter rocking his whole body like a dancing Santa Claus.

'Wow. I mean, that does sound quite irresponsible,' Elle says matter-of-factly, to Billie's surprise and pleasure.

'Just making life a little more interesting,' George says, a twinkle in his eye. Billie has noticed that very wealthy

136

people, of the kind she has met many more of since coming to university, seem to have the same drive to intentionally put themselves in dangerous situations, presumably to re-introduce the stakes that having a lot of money has taken out of their lives. Olivia and George give a detailed account of the first time they saw Tom's advert on the television, and proclaim their love for Tom and for the animated donkey, which leads them neatly into stories about their sons' various nativity play crises. Billie laughs in the right places.

On the rink, she tries her best to stay moving, and skate unsupported. She looks over at the edges of the rink, where those who have failed to prove themselves on the ice have washed up, clinging to the plastic walling. It's important that she does not end up among them. When she passes Angus, roughly once every couple of minutes, he lifts up his phone to take a picture of her. At one point, Angus's father sweeps up behind her and shakes her briefly with a hand on each of her shoulders, which causes her to let out a small but real scream. He skates fluidly around her as she jerks and shudders forward.

'You keeping Angus on the straight and narrow, are you?'

She doesn't know what he means but it seems appropriate to agree. He gives her a broad grin.

'A hard worker, that's what we like to hear. Good girl.'

George calls women of all ages, including his wife and wait-resses, 'good girl', and it makes Billie's teeth clench beneath her smiles.

'What's on the slate for next term?'

'Property, I think.'

George gives a great series of guffaws and mimes shooting himself in the mouth before embarking on a spiel about how boring property law is that Billie has heard at least twice before now.

'You won't want to go into that anyway, pass the damn thing and forget about it,' George says.

George assumes that she wants to be a lawyer – which she does not – because he is a lawyer. She appreciates that he puts effort into approaching her like she is someone worth talking to, though. As though she is someone with dreams and ambitions. She doesn't have these. She only has day-to-day things like getting up and going to lectures, sleeping and eating. Her thoughts don't extend into the future beyond the next end of term. One day, she will get a job, somewhere, doing something. When she pictures herself as an adult, she looks like a slim, plain woman from an office-wear catalogue, wearing low heels and a blazer. She is always completely still. On the other side of the rink, Alfie picks up Elle and throws her over his shoulder, and she pretends that she wants to be put down.

Eventually enough fun has been had, and they all stagger their way off the ice and back into their shoes. Billie feels the awkward solidness of the ground beneath her feet as she walks to the toilet. Olivia catches up with her, announcing her intention to visit the ladies too, and threading an arm through Billie's.

'I just wanted to say how grateful we are to you, sweetheart,' she says, as they wash their hands in adjacent sinks. 'Such a lucky boy to have you to take care of him.'

Billie returns her smile. She looks back at her hands, her fingers turning red as they thaw, passing over and between each other, burning under the lukewarm water.

They get on the bus home, Angus lurching around unable to hold onto anything for support until she guides him into a seat. As they cross Waterloo Bridge, she receives a text from Olivia. It says that Billie should feel like she can talk to her any time, and ends with the kiss-blowing emoji. She shows it to Angus, expecting him to explain it, but he smiles.

'That's nice.'

'Why does she want to talk to me?'

'Oh I guess she – I mentioned your dad and stuff before, so I guess she wants to be helpful. If she can.'

Billie has always sensed that because Angus feels comfortable talking to his mum, he assumes other people will also feel that way.

'Right. Well, that's nice of her but . . . Yeah. I'm fine.'

'She's good at feelings and stuff,' Angus says, with persuasion in his voice. 'And there shouldn't be a stigma about it anyway.'

He pauses for a moment and then says, 'It's okay not to be okay.'

'What, did you read that on the back of a toilet door?' she says, and they both flinch from the tone of her voice.

'Sorry,' she says, her heart sinking. 'Sorry, I don't—'

'I just wanted to like—'

'No I know—'

'—to say it's okay.'

Billie looks out of the window for somewhere else to look.

'Okay. Well, I mean obviously, yes.'

She tries not to feel irritated. She pictures Angus standing naked with bin bags around his hands on the ward where her dad had lived for a while, an image so incongruous that she comes close to actually laughing. She looks over at him, sees that he is watching for her to speak, and turns to look out of the window.

'People say that,' she starts, still looking out at the shop-fronts instead of at Angus, 'and they think they mean it, but it's not ...'

She searches for something concrete.

'It doesn't cover people like my dad. They don't actually think that. They think they do but they don't.' She feels a familiar plug of frustration in her throat. 'I'm not explaining it well.'

'Okay,' she hears him say, and turns to see him nodding to show he's still with her.

'He's not ...'

She wants to say he's not a bad person, but she doesn't say that. She doesn't know how to present the mobius strip of her feelings to Angus, the love that is hate that is love, doubling back and turning in on itself, over and over again. The not knowing makes her angry.

'It's not that simple, Angus.'

'Okay.'

She hates catching herself using his name like this, like it means 'idiot'. They don't speak for a while, but he puts one of his casts into her lap, and she laces her fingers through his, stroking them gently.

After a New Year's Eve party, Billie goes home with a flat-faced guy she chooses almost at random, and when she tells Angus about it, he breaks up with her. She is happy for people to think that this happened because she is cut-throat, an ice queen, when really what she had seen confirmed in those weeks of washing and feeding and nurturing Angus was that she is the kind of person who could very easily shrink away into nothing in the service of someone else's needs.

12

The cemetery at Montparnasse isn't a beautiful place. It's in the middle of a city, and it feels that way, like a place that is striving to be calm rather than somewhere inherently peaceful. There are high stone walls around it, but they don't quite keep out the whine of motorcycles from the road. Billie looks up a map of the cemetery online, and finds Beckett's grave in the orderly grid of death.

When she reaches it, it's underwhelming. A slab of what looks like granite lies there, differentiated from those around it only by its high shine, and a few tributary pens left at its foot. The inscription tells her he died in 1989, which she thinks could be the year her parents met. It could even be a year they were living in France. She doesn't know much about their lives together before she and Tom were born. It had never felt like a good time to ask. But she has seen a few pictures of them from this period, in their dated collars and shorts, glowing with new love and the adventure of moving abroad for no reason. It has always been unimaginable to her that these photographs depict the same people as the people who showed them to her.

She takes a picture of the grave reflexively, knowing that she will never look at it again or show it to anybody. She sits down on a bench looking out across the graveyard and considers the fact that her dad might have a tombstone. She wonders what it would say on it. Mary-Jean would decide, she supposes. 'Loving father and husband'? Something about him being missed? Something flat and evasive, in any case. When she has thoughts like this, she expects to cry, but for whatever reason these aren't the moments when she cries. Her father's face carved in marble relief flashes in her mind, stuck forever in a rictus grin. Surely not one of those.

She googles Samuel Beckett. Black and white images of a deeply cragged face appear. She taps through his Wikipedia to the page for the actress Billie Whitelaw.

Whitelaw remained the foremost interpreter of the man and his work. She gave lectures on the Beckettian technique, and explained, 'He used me as a piece of plaster he was moulding until he got just the right shape'

Billie searches for a video she's seen before, but not for many years. A performance by her namesake, of a play, although she wouldn't know if it's right to call it that. It's on YouTube, and she presses play, spinning her phone around to make it larger. It's playing out loud, but there's nobody around except a pair of elderly ladies eating ice creams over by the tomb of Serge Gainsbourg.

She has a sharp memory of the first time her dad had

showed the video to her, when she was about eight years old. Billie didn't like it then, and she doesn't like it now. The disembodied mouth, the shocking white teeth, the hideous, sphinctral muscularity of the lips. The spit down her chin. The cackling laughter.

Billie has never really understood what 'Not I' is about, but it makes her feel uncomfortable. In the background, the video hisses and drones with age. The mouth speaks in a strange, harsh tone, too fast to keep up with. There are snatches of a story being told among the screams and the disjointed cries of things like 'the brain!' and 'imagine, not suffering!', but she can't follow them, or piece them together into anything coherent. It's only fifteen minutes long but she finds it almost unbearable to watch it through until the end. She makes herself do it.

She doesn't have much time for plays in general. They make her bored and restless. But these plays, by this man, seemed to say something to her father. Or said something to the world that he also wanted to say. She hates that she isn't smart enough to understand exactly what that thing is.

The video finishes. Billie sits on the bench for a while, looking up the avenue at the old women who are casting around in mock despair for a bin to put their sticky ice cream cups in. It occurs to her that it is probable her dad has been here before, not just in this graveyard but at this grave. She thinks about ghosts.

The sun is out and she gets too warm, sweat tickling the soft insides of her arms. When she decides she can't justify sitting there any longer, she leaves the cemetery and walks what she thinks is broadly north up another wide, tree-lined road. She's unsure where she's going. It's a hot day and the streets smell like urine and leaves. She tries to enjoy the walk. Crossing a complicated intersection, she spots and changes course towards a McDonald's, because Tom isn't here to judge her for not having a horsemeat soufflé or whatever he would consider an appropriately local lunch. She orders a Big Mac meal off a screen, glad not to have to talk to anybody, and opts to get a beer with it, feeling a faint ripple of novelty pass through her at the idea. There's a counter seat at the window that she takes her food to, and it is squeezing the ketchup dispenser into the little paper cup that makes her start to cry, for the simple reason that her dad loved ketchup, and now he doesn't love anything. She's already laid all her food out at the counter table and feels too self-conscious to gather it all up and take it to the nice park on the other side of the roundabout, which she now realises is what she should have done all along, so she sits and cries as gently as possible while she eats. A man stops at the window outside and looks long enough to let her know he wants to meet her eyes, so she stares resolutely into her chips until he loses interest and goes away.

Eventually there's no more food and she's pretty much done crying. She decides to walk through the park on the off chance that she feels better on the other side of it. It's grander than it looked from inside McDonald's, more like the gardens of a stately home than a park. Billie's phone tells her that's exactly what it once was. The trees look stiff and formal. She wanders towards a fountain. There are middle-aged men sailing remote control boats, holding onto the pretence that it's for the amusement of their children who are busily kicking a tree several metres away. She sits down on a bench to watch the boats and the kicking. She wonders if she'll ever be good at being in her own company. She has no idea what other people do when they're on their own, whether they feel like they're observing themselves like she does.

Billie reads the same page of her book twice and then gives up and watches videos online. She watches one called 'World's Nicest Car Horn' and holds the phone speaker up to her ear to hear it. It is a nice car horn. A text arrives from Tom.

What are you like with enclosed spaces?

She considers this.

fine I think? why

He types and she thinks about a friend of hers who got stuck in a lift for five hours and had to pee into the dregs of a Frappuccino.

Basically Wayne and Noémie have been wanting to go to the catacombs for a while, but apparently they're gonna go tonight and it should be quite weird and fun if you're up for it

A follow-up message appears.

Noémie has been loads before and knows the deal etc

She frowns at the screen.

who are these people?

Wayne Wayne! and Noémie also works in the pub with me, they're my work friends

They're tunnels under the city, supposed to be v cool but hard to get to if you don't know how to do it bc it's illegal

Billie is picturing sewers. She types.

sounds shit to be honest

She deletes the message. She googles 'Paris catacombs' and her face falls. She sends him one of the pictures of what looks like an enormous barrel made of row upon row of human skulls.

with dead bodies in them . . . ??

She imagines telling Laura that she's gone to Paris to wander around in open graves before her father's funeral and appreciates the image of her appalled expression.

Nonono that's the tourist bit. The rest of the tunnels are just tunnels, no bones. Q cool stuff down there apparently, sculptures etc

147

She stares across the fountain at the dads, now guiding the children in how to pilot the boats. She feels this is the sort of thing she should say yes to.

do you want to?

She watches him type.

Yeah why not!

Have to put phone away now but meet me at the apt at half 6 we can discuss

see you then x

She scrolls through some more videos and then feels guilty for scrolling through videos in the Jardin de Luxembourg, but doesn't stop. Some time later, her phone buzzes and brings her out of her stupor. She picks up.

'Hi, Mum.'

'Helen said you rang?'

Her mum's voice hums through her. Since she moved in with Helen it has seemed to grow even lower and more soft.

'Yeah.'

'Are you all right? How's Tom?'

'Yeah, fine,' she says. The smallest child who is not interested in boats stomps towards her in jelly sandals and expressionlessly lifts his vest to expose the beige balloon of his stomach. She drags up a smile for him, which seems to be what he was hoping for, because he smiles too and plods away, back to his dad and his boat.

'How are you?' Billie asks.

'Oh, I'm all right. I've been keeping busy, all okay here really,' she says, her voice effortfully buoyant.

'That's good. How's the team?'

Her mum updates her with the details of injuries to various ligaments and muscles belonging to the women on the football team she works for. Billie likes to hear her mum using this physiotherapeutic terminology that she herself doesn't understand, likes to let these short monologues wash over her.

When her mum is finished, Billie feels far enough away from her, and far enough outside of normal circumstances to ask.

'How did you do it? With Dad, for all that time.'

She expects a pause. Since they had spoken about the news a week or so ago, checking in with each other over the past seven days more than they had done in the year previously, some barrier had started to break down, although neither of them had yet tried to step over it. But her mother answers immediately, as though she has been expecting the question, and in a tone that suggests the answer has always been obvious.

'I loved him. You just manage, when you love someone. Or you try to, at least.'

Billie makes a noise of agreement.

'And why did you stop?'

'What, loving him?'

'No, trying. Or yeah, I guess loving him.'

The question sounds ridiculous out loud. She doesn't feel

the answer matters, and so isn't sure why she asked. Now her mum sighs, and the silence stretches out.

'I don't know, Billie.' A note of defence has crept in.

'I'm sorry I don't mean to like – I'm . . . ' Billie doesn't know how to explain. ' . . . it's just sad,' she finishes.

'It is sad. I'm sad he's gone.'

'Are you?'

'Of course. He was your father.' Another pause, and her voice comes back more gentle. 'It's complicated, of course it is. But yes, I am sad.'

Billie wants to ask her much more, to follow her down this path while it seems to be clear. The seconds are running out before a change of subject, but she feels weak, sinking heavily into the bench. A silence follows.

'Well, what are you doing over there?' her mum asks brightly.

'Fuck all, really. Sight-seeing a bit. Eating.'

'Good. Good to distract yourself.'

She remembers that Ravi and Angus also said this and thinks again that she doesn't agree. Distracting herself from it feels like cheating.

'Yep.'

'Go on, try to enjoy yourself.'

'Okay.'

'Love you. Bye now,' her mum whispers, and the phone beeps to signal that she's gone.

Billie checks the time, and then finds herself googling 'things to do in Paris' and letting her eyes pass over blog posts and listicles. She decides to go back to the apartment and wait for Tom to finish work instead. Ideally, she wants to put her hands around a warm mug of tea and do nothing, but she thinks about Tom's cheap kettle and feels a scratchy irritation with him. As she approaches the metro station, a girl with a short fringe and two schoolchildren trotting along in her wake stares at Billie until she disappears beneath the pavement.

13

There's a policeman sitting on Billie's bed. The policeman's name is Brian, or maybe Ben. She's not sure, and doesn't want to ask him to say it again. She is also sitting on her bed, and they're both looking out into the room, which is handy because she doesn't want to look at him. Opposite them is a World Wildlife Fund poster of some lions that has been there for a long time, so she's looking at that instead. She thinks it's strange that the WWF does animal rescues as well as wrestling matches, but that's part of why she likes them. There are two lions, a big one and a smaller one, lying on a rock. She and her brother named the lions Catherine and Anne years ago because he had insisted that they were both female lions, although she didn't know at the time how he could tell, and because he had been learning about Henry VIII at school.

The policeman looks too young to be a policeman. When she got a look at him earlier, when he knocked and came into her room, he looked about the same age as Tom, who is fifteen. But he must be older than that because he definitely is a policeman; he's wearing a chunky black vest thing and has gadgets around his belt. She can feel the weight of him on her bed, although they're not touching. He's about an arm's length away from her. She realises that this is the first male person not in her family to sit on her bed, and she wonders whether that matters or not. It's her fault that the policeman is here. Billie didn't expect that he would come, because she hadn't said her address on the phone. She wants to ask him how they knew it was her, how they got there so quickly, but she thinks it's better if she talks to him as little as possible.

Brian or Ben asks her what her name is, so she tells him because that seems like safe information to give. Seeing as they did the trick with the phone call, they can probably find out her name with police computers anyway. He says that Billie is a cool name. This is not true. It's her name because it's also the name of a woman who was in some plays by a man her dad likes called Samuel Beckett. It's a stupid name that people are always asking her about, and she doesn't have anything interesting to say about it or about Samuel Beckett.

The policeman wants to know why she called the police before, so she tells him that it was a mistake, and thanks him for coming. She hopes this will make him get out of her room, but it doesn't. He asks her what happened with her parents and she wants to say the same thing, that it was a mistake, but she's worried that will make him think she's hiding something. She isn't, really, because they were only having an argument, which is normal. Billie lets the silence go on too long because she's choosing between words for 'fight' that sound the least bad. She decides to say they were having a disagreement. It was a disagreement about whether you should keep jam in the fridge or not, except it had become much bigger than the jam, and then they weren't fighting about jam at all, just fighting. She doubts that either of them would even remember the jam now. She doesn't think it matters where you keep the jam, but nobody asked for her opinion. She wants to know what the other policeman, actually a policewoman, is doing downstairs. She can't hear anything through the floor.

The policeman wants to know who started it. It's easy for Billie to get this question right – the answer is 'nobody' – which is good because she didn't get it right before about the phone call. Her mum had told her to make the phone call, but her dad had told her not to. She kept putting the 9 in three times and pressing the green phone button but then pressing the red phone button straight away. This way, she could do what she was told. She could do both. The last time, she had put the phone up to her face and heard a woman asking if she wanted policemen, firemen or an ambulance and she hadn't been able to speak at all, just stand there with the phone to her face and watch the fighting get worse. She couldn't look away or hang up the phone or speak.

One winter, when they had gone to visit her aunt in Scotland, she and Tom had gone tobogganing on the hill behind the house. She had volunteered to go first, sliding down the hill on an oven tray, but the slope was steep and she had lost control and slammed into the back of the house at the end. The slam was so hard that for a while she couldn't move her body, so she lay there in the snow and waited for someone to help her. That was the feeling she had when she was stuck on the stairs with the phone. Except after the toboggan incident she got a hot chocolate and everyone, even

154

Tom, was nice to her, unlike this time. Tom isn't even here. He's probably at his girlfriend's house.

The policeman tells her why he doesn't think 'nobody' is a good answer, but she can't be tricked like that. She doesn't know how to explain the only thing she wants to say, which is that her dad isn't how the policeman thinks he is, so she says nothing. The policeman moves his foot a little, and she notices a smear of jam from his shoe that has been rubbed into her carpet. He must have trodden in some of it when he came through the kitchen, and she sees him notice it now as well, but he doesn't say anything and neither does she. It's so bright red that it embarrasses her.

Downstairs, the front door slams. The policeman hears it too and starts explaining to her that the policewoman will have asked her dad to go out for a while on his own. The policeman tells her that she shouldn't worry, and she acts like she agrees with him. He gives her a little card with a phone number on it and she sees that his name is Brynn with a y and two n's, which actually is a cool name, unlike hers. She puts the card on her bedside table carefully so that its edges line up with the table's corner, so he will think she's grateful for it. She'll wait until the policeman is gone, and then tear it into small pieces and slot each piece into the Diet Coke can in her bin. This means that nobody will see the card except perhaps the bin men, and they won't know what it is anyway because it will be all torn up.

The policeman has been talking but she was thinking about the bin. She nods because there is a pause for her to nod into, but she doesn't know what he said. The nod seems to be OK though, because the policeman smiles at her and stands up, which makes her sink down a bit on the bed. He stands there for a second looking too big in her room, and then Brynn goes out.

Billie listens to him thudding down the stairs, and stares at the lions. She wonders how long lions live for, and hopes that the fact that this poster has been here for ages doesn't mean that Catherine and Anne are dead now. She waits until she hears the front door shut again, so she knows it's only her and her mum left in the house. When her dad is in the house she needs to know exactly where he is, and she's good at working it out. But he's not here now. The silence feels different, heavier.

She goes out onto the landing and stands there for quite a long time. She has no idea about what she should do next. She tries to do nothing, to stand and be as still as she can be, which it turns out is pretty still, but never completely still.

She goes downstairs and finds her mum sat in the mess on one of the kitchen chairs. She takes Billie's hand and tells her she's sorry, that she should not have asked her to call the police. It was the wrong thing to do, because the police won't help her dad. Her mum strokes her hair and kisses her head. They can only take him away, she says, which is not what she and Billie want. Billie nods for her mum. She thinks they should really start to clean up the jam. Jam is so sticky and a real nightmare to clean off floors and surfaces if you leave it for too long.

The oven mitt was a mistake. It's all dripping out of the bottom onto Tom's shoes, he can feel it, but he can't move the mitt or his feet out of the way. He thinks he's in the kitchen.

He needs to move, but if he moves he'll be sick again, and the oven mitt won't take much more. He needs to find something else to throw up into on the way to the bathroom. There's nobody else in the kitchen, but there will be soon. He stands propped up against the counter with his eyes closed, spiralling around for another few seconds, and lurches towards the drying rack. This dish thing, no, a colander, absolutely not, a saucepan. It's in his hands now and he feels the gallop of vomit rising and he's been sick inside it, but somehow he's already in the bathroom hugging the toilet bowl and resting his face on the rim. It's so cold on his cheek. It's wonderful. He will stay here for the rest of his life. He's sick again with a Doritos Chilli Heatwave tang. Something is on his face, and someone's hand wipes it away. His own hand, he thinks. He has too much spit in his mouth so he rolls his head further into the toilet and dribbles at the water. Where's the saucepan? Oh God, or the oven mitt. Where did that go? One of his feet is crushed under what might be his bum or other leg, but when he tries to move his ears slosh. He's sick with a loud echo like being sick in an art gallery.

A sound trickles into his brain of a knocking somewhere far away or a long time ago. A voice says his name. He either replies, or makes a gurgle, or maybe the toilet made that noise. There's someone in the room now very near him, it could be Priya. She wants him to move, but he won't move, not while the toilet seat feels so good on his face. He shuts his eyes. She says his name, and there's a glass of water at his lips, then he retches and vodka, pasta, chocolate buttons sting his throat.

He hears the sound of Priya's brother's voice, low and

soothing. Yes: he remembers now that the party is happening in their house. The party that's still happening, the whump and clink of it washing into his ears from downstairs. They remove him from the toilet against his will, and he's lifted up onto his feet. He throws up down his sweatshirt, but there's not much vomit left and it's not even his sweatshirt now that he looks at it. Then he's alone on his side in the dark of a bedroom, and the pillow smells fresh and peaceful. The sound of his breathing through his nose roars in the room. He breathes through his mouth instead: in, out, in and out until the alcohol closes in and drowns him in sleep.

A growing light makes his eyelids rasp open and pinch shut. He heaves his thoughts back to the night before and tries to squash them together. There was a car, songs on the radio and shouting. Potentially he lost something? He gropes a hand along his waistband and doesn't feel his phone. It could be any time of day. He listens for voices elsewhere in the house, but hears nothing. There's an acrid feeling in his mouth and he is grateful that he is at least empty of sick. He needs to go home, ideally without being seen by anybody. It is likely that he embarrassed himself. Then he feels the toilet bowl chill on his face again, and is sure that he embarrassed himself.

He picks his way down the stairs and clears a path through the party detritus. In a gesture towards relieving his guilt for not staying to help Priya clean up, he peels a piece of pizza off a countertop as he passes through the kitchen and places it on the overflowing bin. On his way to the front door, he registers that he's cold, and spots his jacket slumped over the arm of a sofa in the living room, a can of cider leaking stickily onto its sleeve. He scoops it up and looks in the pockets. The phone is there, but it's dead. The clock on the wall tells him it's quarter to ten. He knows that he was supposed to be home last night, and that his mum will definitely be up by now, but might not have gone to wake him up yet. Or, she's been frantically calling his dead phone for hours already. He feels an ache of remorse for giving her another thing to worry about. It occurs to him now that Abby probably will have texted him too, and his lack of reply will make him look like a bad boyfriend if she tells her friends about it, which she certainly will. He fumbles around at the wall socket and finds a charger. Sitting hunched on the arm of the sofa waiting for his phone to come back to life, he notices that there is somebody asleep on the armchair on the other side of the room. They shuffle slightly but don't wake up. He stares at the narrow black rectangle until it's replaced by a message from Abby, sent an hour or so ago.

You weren't being very nice to me last night.

He searches his memories and comes up dry, but a new knot in his stomach tells him she's right. The person asleep on the armchair turns themselves over in a great, thrashing effort, and Tom sees Sean's face, smudged with disturbed sleep. He opens his eyes.

'What time is it,' he says, his voice low and assured in his half-awake state. Sean has become known lately for his yodelling voice breakage.

'Ten.'

'Shit,' he says, pushing himself up in the chair. He pauses there, hunched over, looking at his socks with a grim expression.

'I'm leaving now if you want to come,' says Tom.

Sean takes a steeling breath and nods.

'I'm gonna wait outside. It smells in here.'

On the street, Tom tries dully to surface more detail about Abby and his behaviour. Nothing comes. He remembers her being there early on, when it was still light outside, and then there are only lurid snapshots of toilet and floor. He hears the door clunk behind him and turns to see Sean holding a half-eaten slice of pizza that Tom hopes is not the one he put on top of the bin.

'Okay,' says Sean, 'let's ride.'

The bus journey is long and slow, and after Sean has given him an account of all the sloppy hook-ups and arguments Tom missed, mostly they don't speak. They catch the tang of each other's clothes every time they turn a corner.

'My mum's going to kill me,' Sean says at intervals, his temple pressed against the bus window in supplication. 'This is the end.'

Sean's house is further up the same street but this route drops them nearer Tom's end. As they walk the final stretch, Sean becomes more agitated, groaning with small agonies. Tom sees from a distance that the front door to his house is open.

'Oh shit,' says Sean.

Tom looks around wildly, expecting to see his mum getting out of the car with shopping and bracing himself to apologise. But the car is there, locked and empty.

'Sneak in, go go go!' Sean goads him, shoving his shoulder.

Could he do that? Go straight upstairs to his room, change out of his clothes and pretend he's just woken up? He doesn't have much to lose. But at the moment he decides to make a break for it, he sees the front door swing open wider. Tom stands stupid and immobilised for a moment before Sean pulls him in behind a van. Tom looks at his friend and sees that the excitement of this has revived him.

'Okay, now, run,' Sean whispers.

Tom peers around the van and catches the back of his dad disappearing around the corner. Dread clenches in his stomach. He can read his dad's body language even in this split second, and at long range. Only now does he see the police car parked halfway up the road. A jolt of anger runs through him. He tries to breathe through it, standing here with one foot on the pavement while it charges around his body. Sean pushes him playfully in the back and the anger surges.

'Fuck off, Sean.'

Sean draws back a little.

'All right, Jesus. Chill out.'

Then the anger begins to seep away, mostly because he's tired and hungover and reeks of old Strongbow and vomit, and sweat, and all it leaves in its place is embarrassment that Sean is here to witness this. Whatever charade the police are currently involved in at his house, pretending to be able to do anything to help, he wants no part in it. It won't matter now that he didn't come home last night, and he knows what kind of atmosphere he will find inside the house: a thick, clamping silence. He sees Sean look for a moment at the police car.

'I need to go back to the high street,' Tom says. This seems too strange a statement on its own. 'I have to run an errand.'

The phrase 'run an errand' seems so obviously borrowed from somebody middle-aged that his face flushes with it.

'Okay,' says Sean, no expression on his face.

'See you,' Tom says as he leaves.

'You're all right, yeah?' Tom hears Sean say to his back.

'Yep,' Tom says without turning around.

He keeps walking. He feels that it would be appropriate and cinematic to have a cigarette, but he regrets it as soon as it's lit and throws it in the gutter half smoked. He buys himself a box of chicken wings with a pound he finds in his pocket. His elbows stick to the table as he drags out the eating to take up as much time as possible. The wings are hot and greasy, and he begins to feel a little better. Tom thinks about his dad walking somewhere within a mile's radius of him. He's too tired to be alert to his moods today, to tiptoe around them.

Eventually he has to admit that there's no more meat anywhere on the chicken bones, and trudges back towards the house. There's not much else he can do with a near-dead phone and no money. The police car is gone when he returns, and the street is quiet. Tom unlocks the door. He can see his mum filling the kettle, and Billie sat at the kitchen table picking her nails through the door at the end of the hall. Wanting to know what happened and not wanting to know anything about it wrestle in him, but he's desperately thirsty and needs to get a glass of water. Billie doesn't look up as he comes in, but his mum makes herself smile, and says hello and calls him sweetheart.

There's smashed glass and chunks of red goo spattered all over the floor, gummed up in the gap between the counter and the fridge, staining the wall in streaks. He looks at his mum. She is blotchy and drained but he can't see any obvious signs of anything worse. A wave of pity flows through him but it's followed by a harder, more bitter feeling. He asks her whether this will keep happening and nudges a piece of glass around the tile with the toe of his shoe. She says that it's just a bad patch and nobody says anything back.

Billie's chair screeches and she begins to pick up bits of a jar with a careful thumb and forefinger. She won't meet his eye. Tom starts to pick up the glass too, and the only sounds in the room are the gentle clink of tile on shard, and the rumbling of the kettle. They are repairing the scenery, rebuilding the set on which their performance of normal life takes place.

When the floor is clean, Tom makes a sandwich in silence, wishing that he wanted to comfort his mum, and takes it upstairs to his bedroom. Late that night, after his mum comes back from a long run, he hears her through the floor, talking to God in the living room.

14

He feels a little embarrassed to have fallen in love in Paris. It hadn't featured in even the most naïve fantasies he had of living here. And yet, here he is spending his days at work wound up in anticipation of seeing her in five, four and a half, four hours. Trying not to mention her in too many conversations with his co-workers, rationing himself to texts sent from the toilets and an ever-increasing number of cigarette breaks. He carries around the knowledge of their happiness like a small animal in his pocket, something warm, soft and secret. When the last orders bell goes, it feels like it clangs inside his own chest.

She also lives in a maid flat, owned by the American family she nannies for. It's more modern than his, and seems like a bigger room if only because the bed is in an alcove that makes it feel separate from the kitchen and living space. He more or less moves in. They spend the winter moving in a pack around the apartment: him, her and the heater on wheels, from bed to stove to table.

They met through an app in Tom's first few weeks in Paris. He was familiar with the rhythms of app dating from home. The first-and-last dates with women who were very interesting but not attractive to him, the loose arrangements between him and the people he met there that came together and fell apart easily, satisfying but in a muted and unmemorable way. He was settling into the role of the casual dater, and didn't have any particular expectations of Nour, twenty-four. They went to a bar in the 11th that she'd picked. It was loud, eccentrically lit in deep red and full of gothic-accented furniture. The table they sat at had a dripping candle on it in the shape of a skull. Her fringe was cut well above her eyebrows but she kept nervously sweeping it out of her face as she leant forwards to talk to him. He found it endearing that she was nervous. She talked about her nannying and the writing it paid for her to do in her spare time, he talked about how awful the English are for comic effect, and they went home together.

It was fun, but it wasn't until late that night that Tom had begun to think she might be special. At two or three in the morning, he had got up to use the bathroom. Nour had told him to just pee in the sink, but some deep-seated knot of reserve told him he should insist on using the toilet, even though he peed in his own sink as a matter of routine. He had crept out onto the staircase in his boxers and down a flight, where he then managed to lock himself inside the toilet. He stood there holding the part of the latch that had come off in his hands, looking at it agog, as though it might tell him what to do. He had no means of telling the time, but it felt like at least half an hour before Nour decided that he wasn't taking a shit and that something was probably wrong, and a further half hour after that before the noise of them trying to cave the door in woke up her employers. An American voice introduced itself through the door as Todd. Eventually Todd managed to take the lock mechanism apart from the outside with an expansive tool kit. While he was trapped, Tom ran through the ways he would be likely to react to someone forcing him to wake up his boss in the middle of the night to let them out of his toilet, half naked. None of them included pure delight, and so he was surprised to find Nour cackling with glee once he was safely back inside her room. Lying in bed, they agreed that this was the kind of thing that meant either they would have to never see each other again, or be together forever, and each of them silently leant towards the same option.

She is prone to fits of hysterical laughter. Somebody once sent her a picture of a snake wearing a paper top hat which had cast some kind of spell on her that made her laugh until she cried. He now loves the stories he had hated most about his life, about the scare attraction and the mortifying auditions, because she finds them funny. In any case, they belonged to the world before Nour, a time so distant that the stories no longer even feel like they are about the same person. They are just currency he has banked to spend on entertaining her. The two of them perform an ironic disgust at their dumb happiness for other people, but he doesn't think it's very convincing. Nour is better at it than he is. She likes to joke in company that the only thing she likes about Tom is that he's not French, which has the added benefit for her of annoying her male friends, who are all French.

They are lying on her bed together one afternoon in April, having watched *The Prince of Egypt* on her laptop, and talking.

'It's strange to think about you at church. Did you wear smart clothes?' she says, picking at a scabbed scratch on his forearm.

'No, not at all. I guess it would have been bad to look really scruffy. But we just wore normal clothes.'

He has a sense memory of the slick feel of the Arsenal shirt he had as a child sliding against his skin.

'Did you go to mosque much?'

'Yeah, sometimes. My grandmother likes me to go with her, but it's boring.'

'Church was mostly boring, yeah. I don't know. I stopped going when I was like twelve.'

'Did your parents not care?'

'It was only Mum who went. I think she did mind a bit. But we didn't argue about it. She's not a very argu-ey person.'

'Why did you stop going?'

He notices his breathing, heavy and slow. It lifts the forearm she has resting on his chest up, and then drops it down. He lets his eyes pass over some railings he can see out of the window.

'I had this weird thing at the Sunday school.'

'Sunday school is like, kids' church?'

'Yeah, there was a room upstairs and we'd do crafts and watch these Christian cartoons on a shitty TV. There was one where a load of animated vegetables act out scenes from the Bible. And also songs about brushing your teeth, stuff like that.'

'Bible vegetables,' Nour repeats.

167

'Yep.'

He feels her waiting in the silence he's left. He lines up the story and realises he has never told it before.

'There were these two boys who also came to our church sometimes. Owen and . . . something. One week the teacher was dealing with some problem with the younger kids, and the three of us snuck outside. There was a patch of grass by the carpark and we went to sit on it. They were talking about the teacher being weird or whatever, and she did used to close her eyes while she was talking for really long periods.'

'That is kind of weird.'

'Well, not really, but we were twelve-year-old boys so it was weird enough. Anyway, they got on to the subject of weird teachers more generally, and Owen started talking about his cousin, who told him this story about a teacher at his school.'

Tom notices his neck start to feel hot.

'And the story was about a teacher who everyone already thought was a bit off, and somehow I knew then that he was talking about my dad.'

Nour makes a noise of compassion into his chest, and he carries on because he's started now.

'Then this boy, Owen, said that one day a girl was texting in class and the teacher, my dad, flew into a rage and took the phone and threw it against the wall. And it smashed, and all the kids freaked out and the girl was really upset. Then he didn't come back to school after that.'

'Mmm,' she says, and he hears her keeping her tone neutral. He feels an itchy sensation, but he's spurred by an unfamiliar force to continue.

'And my dad did stop teaching around then, but I didn't know why. I didn't want them to know that they were talking about my dad so I laughed. But then Owen used his name. He said "Mr Perrin", and looked at me. I didn't know for sure whether he knew what my second name was, but why would you remember the name unless it rang a bell? So I told them I needed the toilet and got up and went home.'

'Then you didn't go any more?'

'Yep. Around then.'

Nour waits for him to carry on speaking. To his own surprise, he does.

'It made me feel really small. And embarrassed.'

She rubs his chest, and he feels the ache of trying to articulate himself. Embarrassed isn't right.

'Ashamed, I guess. I don't think I'd really considered before then how my dad behaved with other people. What he might be doing when he wasn't with us.'

Nour is silent for a few seconds.

'We can talk about your dad, if you want to?'

He kisses her on the head.

'It's okay. Thank you.'

And broadly, it is okay. He pictures himself trusting her with more stories like this one, telling her things as they lie in this same position in her bedroom. The scene is realistic. He looks happy in it.

They are quiet for a while.

'When will I meet them?'

'I don't know. I expect my mum will come and visit, and my sister at some point.'

'Or I could come to London?'

'My mum's not in London any more.'

Tom realises she doesn't know this and it displaces him. He sees his mum, long and greyhound-lean, her bush of hair scraped away from her face. He misses her. A beat too late, he hears how this will have sounded to Nour.

'But it would be great if you came, I'd love you to come. Just – yeah. She lives with her sister near Glasgow now.'

'Okay. That's nice for them.'

'It's complicated but yeah, I think it is nice.'

Nour leaves him space to explain, but he decides to leave this one for another day.

'Billie is in London, but we couldn't stay with her. I mean we could, but she lives with all these boring corporate people.'

'What do they do?'

He searches his mind but he doesn't know. He isn't in fact sure that this is accurate, now that he thinks about it. 'You know, city jobs.'

Nour readjusts herself so that her feet are no longer tucked under the duvet. She frowns slightly, and he understands the confusion.

'As in, corporate jobs. Business stuff.'

'Aha, business stuff. Not important stuff like serving beers.'

He pokes her lightly in the ribs and she squirms away, pleased at having gotten a rise out of him.

'No, not important stuff like what you do,' he says.

'Writing?' He feels her shrug. 'Imagine the world with only writers in it. No thank you.'

She sits up and shuffles to sit against the wall with her legs thrown over his torso. She gathers her hair to put it in a

170

ponytail, then realises she doesn't have a tie and lets it fall to her shoulders again.

'Someone has to do the business stuff,' she says.

'Do they?'

Nour smiles and rolls her eyes at him.

'Don't be boring. I'm hungry, what do you want?'

He blows his lips out, manoeuvres himself out from underneath her and gets up.

'Is there any of the chicken left?' he says, padding towards the fridge.

'No, I ate it at lunch,' Nour says. But he hardly hears her. He's turned towards the window, staring at the sky.

'Look at this,' he says, beckoning to her without looking away. She comes to his side and gasps. There is smoke rolling up from somewhere beyond the rooftops.

'Where is that?' he asks her, and she pulls out her phone and starts to tap.

'*Putain.*'

She lifts the phone to his face and scrolls through the images for him, of Notre Dame blazing red and yellow, the tower funnelling black soot up into the air.

'Oh shit . . . '

Nour thuds across the room and grabs a pair of trainers from under the bed. Tom makes himself look away from the smoke and hesitates.

'It's not like a terrorist thing, is it?'

'No. Come on, quickly, we have to see.'

They get themselves dressed, dodging around each other in the tiny space for jackets and keys. They thunder down the stairs together and out into the courtyard. His hands fumble

171

with misplaced excitement as he unlocks his bike. Out in the narrow street, the smoke is hardly visible, dissipating into the darkening sky.

Nour rides first, weaving around parked mopeds and running red lights as he fights to keep up with her. At every junction he whips his head right to watch the progress of the black cloud rising overhead. On the pavements, people have stopped to look, or are moving towards it to see the source for themselves. The sky opens out as they near the Pont Saint-Michel and Tom's breath catches as he sees the fire itself. They dismount and wheel their bikes into the crowd of people stood transfixed by the sight of the flames swallowing the cathedral tower. Sirens blare over the sound of timber cracking in the distance. Nour raises a hand to her chest, and Tom puts an arm around her.

'You okay?'

'Yes.'

Her eyes are glistening. He rubs her arm in consolation, and she shakes herself out, seeming a little annoyed with herself.

'It's stupid, it's just a building.'

They stand there with the rest of the crowd watching in disbelief. The importance of the event they're witnessing gives Tom a sensation of time warping strangely, of being weightily present in the current moment but also seeing himself as if from the future, at the birth of something significant, a fixed point on a timeline. He tries to summon some sadness to fit the disaster raging in front of him, something to match the way she feels watching this building burn, but he can't. However inappropriate it is, the primary feeling he has is a deep, radiating joy, because watching Nour

172

pedalling furiously ahead of him towards the cathedral, her puffer jacket billowing out in her wake, it had occurred to him that he would like to be following her around for the rest of his life.

15

As always when they are nearing the end of the shift, there is a collective lightening of mood as the day outside darkens. Tom watches a Guinness separate itself, its occult upward cascade.

'What did she say, your sister?' asks Noémie, picking some dried barbecue sauce off the underside of the bar.

'Yeah, I reckon she's up for it.'

Noémie nods soberly. She pulls her order pad out of her back pocket and begins to write. Tom puts the Guinness on the bar, and for the first time feels a warm, corporeal satisfaction that he will be drinking again later.

The pub is empty except for some slightly lost-looking American tourists and a woman who seems to be in the process of being dumped by the guy sitting across from her at the back corner table. This happens quite a lot at the Coq, more so than other bars he's worked in. He thinks it's because it's the kind of place you could happily bring someone to break up with them, safe in the knowledge that neither of you will ever want to come here again anyway, and the music is loud enough to cover a sob. He scans the empty banquettes to see if any of them obviously need a wipe down, if their sheen is looking especially sweaty.

'You need these things. Don't forget,' Noémie says as she tears off the list and gives it to him. Tom scans it.

'What's *caoutchouc*?'

'Boots for the water.'

She catches the look of concern on his face.

'Or old shoes, it doesn't matter.'

Tom and Wayne have been pestering Noémie to show them the tunnels for months now, ever since she described the catacombs to them during one dragging shift when she had turned up looking like she hadn't slept and they demanded to know why. To hear her tell it, the tunnels were a rich labyrinth of wonders, with outsider artwork adorning every surface and an electric atmosphere of anarchy and hedonism. Really, Tom suspects that it's less romantic than this, but his curiosity was piqued enough to want to see it for himself. She has ignored their previous requests to come with her, on the grounds that she doesn't want to babysit them. Tonight, though, the friends from school she was supposed to be going down with have cried off, and Wayne has finally managed to persuade her to take them down instead, on the condition that they 'respect the tunnels'.

When she's not assistant managing the pub, Noémie is doing an internship at an environmental policy think tank. Tom had thought about training to become a manager himself but decided against it when he learned that the programme to do so was called 'Creating Legends'. After a few drinks, Noémie is prone to launching into surly, earnest sermons

175

about human responsibility to the landscape. Tom thinks these speeches, the notion of respecting the tunnels and her internship at the environment agency are all connected, but isn't completely sure because they are an almost uniquely potent trigger for him to zone out.

He feels strangely confident that letting Noémie take them all to the catacombs is a good idea. Billie needs distracting, and Tom needs there to be as little dead time as he can engineer. He had thought that maybe when she was actually here, he would feel more able to talk about things. But still, talking feels impossible. He feels alternately like there is nothing to say, and that there is so much that he can't start, pin-balling between these positions, both of which leave him silent. He has been trying to identify when the last substantive conversation he had with his father was, and coming up dry. Years now of unreturned phone calls, avoided meetings, civil nods. One of the reliefs of living here has been that it puts his distance from his family into a context that makes sense. He is physically elsewhere.

Not that he knows what he is doing here. But not knowing what he is doing in Paris feels more productive than not knowing at home. Every day holds the potential for small triumphs rather than small humiliations. Recognising new words on street signs, holding a successful conversation, navigating a piece of administration as inconsequential as putting something in the post: all of these things are little confirmations that he is not so useless after all. He wonders sometimes if this would do, as a way to spend a life – moving every few years from place to place, staying just long enough to feel that his slotting in is now seamless, and then leaving again. Evading the grasp of roots. He suspects but tries not to think about the suspicion that this would not, in fact, make a life, and that his time feeling good in this particular way, here, will run out.

His phone lights up where it is charging under the bar. Tom moves towards it and swipes the message open with one finger. It's from Sean.

> **Hello mate. Really sorry to hear about your Dad. I hope you're doing okay. It would be great to catch up when you're home for the funeral, but no pressure, obviously. Take care.**

He hates the full-stops, the full sentences.

'Tom?' Wayne's voice calls up from the basement. Tom puts his phone on airplane mode.

'Yep?'

'Barrel.'

Tom lumbers down the steps and into the close, dim space. Wayne unhooks the old beer barrel, dripping remnants onto the pitted floor, and they both manoeuvre the new one into position.

'Is it fun having your sister here?' Wayne says.

'Yeah, sort of. It's not that fun a time, I suppose.'

'No, of course.'

Wayne shakes his head in self-reproach and they hoist the barrel up. 'And how are you doing, with all of it?'

Tom nods in a 'can't complain' sort of way. He doesn't know how to account for the poor quality of his grief, its shrunken, gnarled shape.

'Okay. I mean not really but . . .'

177

He pauses and feels the way he always does when called upon to explain this, like he's skirting around the edge of a pit he doesn't want to climb into.

'Yeah, he wasn't very nice. My dad.'

He hates the way this sounds, teenaged and self-pitying.

'Or like . . . yeah, it's just complicated.'

'Right, yeah,' Wayne says. 'Well, that's dads for you.'

Tom mumbles in agreement.

'Not my dad actually, to be honest. My dad's adorable,' Wayne adds, in a mock-boasting tone.

Tom forces a laugh. He remembers meeting Wayne's dad at a showcase they did once, a smaller, gentler version of Wayne who took them for beers and showed them the pocket pack of tissues he'd brought to cry his fatherly pride into during the performance.

'Do you have a date for the funeral yet?'

'It's in a week.'

Tom means to stop there but some other part of him decides to hear what his thought sounds like out loud.

'I don't think I'll go.'

He looks at Wayne, who wipes the surprise off his face almost fast enough for Tom not to catch it.

'Oh right. Okay.'

They are both silent for a moment.

'You know, think about it,' says Wayne in a careful tone. 'That's a big choice.'

Tom nods at the barrels. He hears the scuffing sound of Wayne passing a hand backwards and forwards over his shaved head, something he does when he is thinking.

'Well, look, I'm here. For you, about it.'

Tom doesn't quite look at Wayne, smiling at the light fitting a few inches to his left instead. Wayne falters for a moment and then resets.

'Okay. I'm gonna scoot off a little early, will you clock me out?'

Tom takes Wayne's fob for the till from him.

'Oh, the guy at the end of the bar with the red shirt on is a nutcase, FYI.'

'What kind?' Tom straightens up and wipe his sticky hands on his apron.

'Oh like, a pervert. He asked me "where my family are from" and then told me about how he lost his virginity in a Beijing botanical gardens.'

'Ugh.'

A look of apprehension passes across Wayne's face.

'But yeah, don't let him rile you up. Probably just drunk.'

Tom knows what Wayne is thinking about. A couple of months ago, Tom had needed to be restrained by Wayne and Rico from throwing a punch at a customer who tried to touch Noémie's chest over the bar. He wasn't even sure if he would have followed through with the punch. He remembers seeing the man reaching for her, but there is a hot, white blank in his memory between that and him being held back with his arm raised as the man laughed at him and turned around to leave. They had all allowed him to blame it on the fact that they were drinking on shift, but he does not like this memory.

'I'll be fine,' Tom says. 'Thank you.'

'Okay, so meet at nine later.'

Wayne kisses his own hand, waves it and leaves Tom alone in the cellar. Back above ground, Tom pretends not to speak

English, and the guy in the red shirt eventually gives up trying to talk to him and turns his attention to cleaning the condiments off his plate with a licked finger.

When he returns to the flat, Tom finds Billie with both her feet up against the wall. The balcony doors are open and there is a strong smell of vinegar in the room.

'Why does it stink in here?'

Billie cranes around to look at him.

'I descaled your kettle.'

He stands there in the tangy air.

'Okay.'

He looks over to the counter top and is relieved to see an empty bottle of white vinegar instead of the balsamic he knows is at the back of the cupboard.

'You're welcome,' she says.

'Yes, thank you.'

He is determined not to let her see that he has interpreted the descaling in the way she meant: as an insult about the way he lives.

'You left the flat, right?' he says.

'Oh yeah I've been everywhere,' she says, swinging her legs down off the wall and pivoting to a sit. 'How was work?'

He makes a noise that doesn't really signify anything, and sits down at the table in a heavy, worn-out sort of way he vaguely feels makes him seem noble. He reads down the list Noémie made.

'Did you bring anything waterproof?' he asks.

Billie looks at her suitcase, calculating.

'No.'

Tom gets back to his feet and starts to search in his cupboard, pulling out moth-eaten sweaters and plastic bags stuffed in other plastic bags.

'What about shoes?'

'I have these,' she says, gesturing to the pair of crisp white and beige trainers on her feet.

'Do you mind ruining them?'

'Obviously, yes. Sorry, where are we going that they'd get ruined?'

'Noémie said it's wet down there and dusty and stuff.'

'Wet and dusty.'

'We don't have to go. Really.'

She rolls her eyes.

'No, go on, it'll be . . . it sounds "interesting".' She puts her fingers around the word again, making fun of herself instead of him this time. 'But yeah, I need some shoes.'

Their sharing a shoe size has been a source of embarrassment for both of them at different stages of their lives: big for a woman, small for a man. He hands her his mankiest pair of plimsolls, their rubber soles peeling away from the canvas. She puts them on and walks awkwardly around what space the room has to offer. They're a little big on Tom too, but they'll do. From the furthest corner of the cupboard he fishes out a luridly purple backpack someone had left in lost property at the pub and that he had won in the annual clear out. She takes it from him and peers inside it warily before slinging it over her shoulder.

'Is it cold down there?' she asks.

'I guess it might be, yeah,' he says as he shakes out a cagoule and examines it. 'Bring another layer in case?'

'Can I borrow something?'

Tom turns back to the piles of things at the bottom of his cupboard, scoops up an assortment of ropey sweaters and puts them on the bed for Billie to look through. She picks through them, rejecting each item until he sees her arrive at the bright turquoise, unworn jumper from Ralph Lauren, and the scarf that goes with it. Tom had meant to try to sell these, but had forgotten about them. Billie's hand lingers over the jumper, feeling the cable knit between two fingers. Tom stands up and takes himself off to the toilet. By the time he's back, the jumper is back at the bottom of the cupboard, and Billie looks a little distant.

'Noémie has one head torch she can lend us but we need something for you ... ' he says, casting around the room.

'Or for you,' she says irritably.

They fashion a head torch out of a couple of bike lights and a beanie. She dutifully puts it on, and sits on the edge of the bed, the lights flashing maniacally at him while she replies to texts in silence.

On the way down to the metro, they pass a man leaning forward onto the railings, who slaps Tom on the arm and says something loudly. He doesn't reply and they continue down the steps.

'What was that?'

'Nothing.'

'Tell me.'

'He said you were beautiful.'

'No he didn't,' Billie says, in a tone half of distaste and half of intrigue.

'Well, what he said was you're "*atypique*".'

She gives him a confused look as he leads them down to the platform.

'Atypical?'

'Like, in a good way.'

As they approach the barriers, Billie fumbles in her pocket for a ticket.

'Why did he tell you?' She realises. 'Oh. Gross.'

'France is quite gross. In some respects.'

With a practised ease, Tom vaults himself over the ticket barrier, knowing and enjoying the knowledge that this will annoy Billie. He turns back to look and sees her resolving not to acknowledge it, and huffily shoving her ticket at the turnstile.

The train pulls in and they muscle their way into the carriage. Billie cranks open a fold-out chair and Tom stands beside her reading from his phone.

'So yeah, only a tiny bit of the tunnels is for bones. The rest used to be quarries.'

Billie nods, and Tom sees her look out through the cloudy glass at the platform, arched over by a half pipe of white tile, but he knows she is looking at her own face, too. She's always looking for her reflection, in car windows and shop fronts, and changes her face slightly as she finds it, a loosening of something in the jaw.

'Those are the tiles I'll have in my kitchen. When I have my own kitchen.'

Tom glances out.

'I can read this in my head.'

She turns her head away from the window.

'Sorry, I'm listening. Quarries.'

Tom goes back to his phone. He scans the page and digests it for her.

'They built most of Paris out of the stone that was underneath Paris.'

They both frown, an identical expression on their faces.

'And then as the city got bigger and bigger in the south, the quarries started caving in under the weight of the buildings.'

Billie thinks.

'So they built stuff on shitty foundations that were shitty because they got emptied out for the stone they made to use the buildings,' she says, tracking this thought with a sequence of hand movements.

'Sounds like it, yeah.'

'Well, that was stupid.'

Billie turns back to the window and raises her eyebrows.

'What's the bit with the bones in it then?'

Tom flicks up and down the page as the train rattles on around them.

'A graveyard got too full and people's basement walls kept collapsing and bodies poured in, so they moved the bones into a part of the catacombs.'

He imagines the cramped and musty space under the stairs in the house where they grew up, opening the door and being confronted with a tide of rotting corpses. In the window reflection he sees his sister grimace.

'Jesus.'

He looks around the carriage, and thinks that one day, the swaying bodies of the Parisians around him, chatting quietly, or reading, or staring into space, will all be matter that needs to be disposed of.

16

Tom's days are long. He falls into the unmade bed on the top floor of his student house every night and feels like he passes out before he hits the mattress. The exhaustion is satisfying. Now, halfway through his second year, his body shows unmistakable signs of its new training. There is a leaner muscularity that he thinks makes him look almost like a ballerina, or a swimmer. He likes to catch sight of his calves flexing as he cycles past shop windows on his way in for class in the early mornings, glowing with a sense of shared purpose between him and the other people on their way to work at this hour. If the students arrive later than 8:50, they get sent home for the day, but he is never late.

When people on his course talk about how lucky he is to have got in on his first try, he puts on a humble face and agrees with them, but in his heart he knows it wasn't luck. Way back in their first week, all the students in his year group gathered in the main theatre. They sat in leggings and leotards and hoodies, contorting themselves on the wooden floor into whatever pose seemed most charismatic. The head of the course, a short, big man called Carlos who commanded total authority, stood in front of them and held out his arms wide, encompassing all the people sitting on the floor. Then he swept his left arm across to almost meet his right, leaving about a person's width between them.

'This is what proportion of you will be working as actors in five years' time. Know that now.'

The room had rippled with discomfort, but Tom was unshaken. Carlos's warning wasn't for him. Every painful experience he has ever had has merely been a contribution to the store of raw elements he will craft into performances, performances that will justify those experiences having taken place. This is what he was born to do. Each morning they begin the day by walking into one of the big, bright rehearsal spaces one by one and announcing their presence. He loves the slap of his bare feet on the wood, and hearing his own voice ring loud around the room saying, 'I am Tom, and I am here'. Anywhere else this would be ridiculous, and he would think it was pompous and stupid. But here, the grandeur feels appropriate to him, because this is the centre of the universe.

He has settled now, into a new city, a new schedule, new friends, a new version of himself to try playing. He had briefly been sleeping with a girl on his course who was herself sleeping with another girl on his course, and none of it had been a big deal. Imagining this kind of thing happening in Palmers Green, with its Catholic schoolgirls, is satisfyingly difficult. He is living in the real, modern world now, and they are not. It's difficult to think of Palmers Green at all. Everything and everybody there is irrelevant.

Today, they've spent all morning doing voice work, perfecting the art of breathing in and out with an intensity of focus he would not have thought possible two years ago. He sits on a bench in the school courtyard while he finishes a cigarette. He soaks up some energy from the winter sun that is filtering through bare trees branched out against the sky, looking like blood vessels on the back of an eyeball. They have a new teacher this afternoon who is doing character work with them, and it will be draining. They never know what to expect with visiting staff. Once, they had a woman from one of the premier drama institutions in Sweden come to spend a term training them to mime getting dressed and undressed in the persona of celebrities. Tom had chosen Tony Blair, not realising he would be confined to this choice for twelve weeks. Sometimes he still catches himself replicating his dead-eyed smile like a nervous tic.

The new practitioner enters the studio in the same gaggle as the students, and establishes himself on a bucket chair. He's a local, he tells them – in fact he grew up down the road near Old Trafford. They're put in pairs and they get started. He wants them to imagine they bear various relations to each other, and to flow through these different states as he shouts them out. Tom is paired with Ksenia, the tallest girl in their cohort. She's handsome and powerful-looking in a way that Tom finds a little too intimidating to be attractive. They move towards, away from and around each other, as siblings, as enemies, as mother and child, as rival football fans. After a while, the practitioner singles out pairs for the rest of the students to watch, and gives them prompts. They watch Wayne and another of the boys pretend to be two colleagues who have received news of the unfair promotion of a third. Then a pair of the girls, who can't stand each other, play an elderly couple at the end of a hard day. The practitioner points to Tom and Ksenia, and they fluidly replace the girls in the centre of the space.

'You are lovers, but it's gone wrong,' he says.

They adapt their manner, tensing.

'You,' he continues, pointing to Ksenia, 'have to stop him from getting up from the bed.' He points at Tom. 'You have to get away from her, however you can.'

Tom does not hesitate. You do as you are told here. He lowers himself to the floor. Ksenia follows him down, and places her body over the top of his. He smells sweat and tea tree.

As Tom lifts his arms to begin to struggle, she moves reflexively to take one of his wrists in each of her hands. She tries to pin down his legs with her knees. She's even stronger than he expected her to be, and her biceps seem to harden over him without effort. He jerks a little to test the power of her grip and meets her eyes. She looks at him coldly.

He begins to thrash, making strong, sharp, movements to try to shake her off. He feels her laboured breath on his face, and the struggle begins to force noises from both of them. The rest of the students are quiet, watching with respectful interest.

'You hate her,' the practitioner says loudly. 'Get her off.'

Tom's whole body strains as he tries harder to get free. She clamps his wrists tighter and bears herself down in response. His heart races.

Ksenia screams, her cry echoing huge in the space around them.

'Don't let him go!' the practitioner shouts, and then Tom's voice is part of the uproar too, shouting at Ksenia to shut up. The noise is deafening in the studio, and Tom notices sweat dampening his T-shirt where it touches the floor. His breath comes shallow and he begins to panic, losing connection to the performance. She looks enormous over him, blocking out the strip lighting.

She screams again, and now something in Tom snaps. He draws a new surge of energy from somewhere inside him and shoves her away with his forearms, unbalancing her. As she falters, he releases himself, pushing her away and getting up onto his feet. Hot rage is flowing through him, and he vibrates with it, alarmed by how quickly it has taken him over.

'Fuck you,' Tom screams at the practitioner, shaking. The rest of the class stare at him. He lunges for his jacket, draped over the back of a chair, and turns for the door. He needs to get out of the room.

'Hey, hey,' the practitioner calls after Tom, who slams his way out of the studio. The door makes a terrible bang as it hits the wall and bounces on its hinges, but it's not enough to shock him out of it. He keeps walking, with no destination in mind except away from the room, breathing as deeply as he can manage. He storms through the corridors, pounding his way through swinging doors with his blood throbbing like it wants to pour out through his ears. When he finally bursts onto the street, the change in acoustics and the total indifference of people walking past him makes him ridiculous. He stalls, feeling both that he has nowhere he wants to go and that he ought to keep going somewhere, that the momentum of the outburst demands it. For several long moments he stands there, paralysed.

'Tom.'

He turns. Wayne is jogging down the steps of the school towards him.

'What's up? What was that?'

He looks concerned but it's mixed with reproach.

'Nothing. I'm sorry,' Tom says. He works to slow down his breathing.

'You don't have to apologise. Well, I mean you probably do have to, but not to me.'

Tom thinks uneasily of Ksenia now, and knows he should have thought of her sooner than this.

'Is she okay?'

'I'm sure she's fine but like . . . ' Wayne looks for words. 'You should try not to do that.'

Tom mumbles in agreement, his face dead with shame.

'Are *you* okay?' Wayne asks.

'Yeah. I'm fine. It's sometimes all a bit intense, you know?'

Wayne gives a tight smile of consolation. It is frequently intense. Last week they had both watched as one of their classmates took their roaming improvisation class too far and had to be stopped by the practitioner from eating rotting food out of a bin behind the main theatre.

'Shall we go back in?'

Tom would prefer to walk into the traffic than go back in, but he nods.

'Let me just – give me a second.'

They stand there for a minute or so while Tom looks out at the road, retreating back into the deep centre of himself where he doesn't frighten anybody and nobody can frighten him. Then he turns towards his friend, and they walk back in together.

He wishes going back to the room didn't involve sheepishly pushing their way back through the same doors he'd slammed not ten minutes ago, but this is the only way to the studio. Most people have already left, the class having just ended, but inside he finds a small handful of his peers standing around Ksenia, who is sat in one of the chairs looking unruffled. The practitioner is there too, and Tom decides to apologise to him first. He endures a short, stern lecture about professional conduct, followed by a softer reminder of the student support services. Then Tom turns to Ksenia, who shrugs it off with an ease that makes him feel a new rush of shame. She leaves, trailed by her entourage, who give him weak smiles or avoid looking at him at all.

'Not so hard, was it?' Wayne says, in a voice edged with something other than sympathy that Tom can't quite read.

The two of them walk together back to the cafe annexe attached to the school canteen, a large, busy room that smells of muffins and deodorant. Tom sits down and allows himself to be enveloped in a corner sofa. Wayne brings him a cup of water and Tom focuses on the liquid running cold in his throat. He trains his gaze on a noticeboard beside them to avoid making eye contact with any of his fellow students meandering in and out of the room. One flyer in particular, for a student stand-up night from last weekend, snags his attention. His stomach drops.

'Wayne, your gig,' he says.

Tom looks over at his friend who gives the noticeboard a

thin smile. He scrambles for a way to undo this mistake even as he knows it's too late and then crumples under a new torrent of self-loathing.

'I thought I would give it a few days and see if you remembered,' Wayne says.

'Fuck, I'm so sorry.'

Wayne nods placidly, as if he is being told something he already knows.

'Yeah, I'm sure. But it happens sometimes, and it's shit, I think.'

Tom hates himself even more as he asks the now-poisoned question.

'How was it?'

'It was fine. Not great. I don't think I'll do it again.'

The lightness of Wayne's tone is more painful to Tom than if he had been angry.

'I'm really sorry.'

Wayne shrugs, not unkindly.

'Yeah.'

They sit in a dense silence. Wayne raps the fingers of one hand against the table smartly, and then starts to get up.

'I'm gonna pee before class, but I'll see you in there?'

Tom nods and Wayne leaves.

After Tom has sat stewing in his own misery for a few more minutes, his phone rings. He ignores the vibrations against his leg at first. When it doesn't stop, he checks the screen. Billie doesn't call him. He weighs it up for a few more rings, and then answers.

'Tom?'

'Yes, what?'

He feels her recoil from his tone.

'Jesus, okay.'

'Sorry, hi. I'm in the middle of something.'

'I'm worried about Mum.'

He sits more still than before, but his heart rises again in his chest.

'Okay.'

'She's been ... ' Billie starts to gain speed, 'things have been really bad here recently, and I don't know, she seems different and today—' her voice lowers a little, '—I came home from school and she'd been running and I saw her feet and they're wrecked. They were bleeding all over the floor and her shoes were covered in it and she tried to hide it from me but yeah, I don't know what I should do.'

Tom breathes. He can't think about it.

'What should I do?' he hears her ask.

'Look, I don't know. I'm sorry, I don't know, I'm having a bad day myself and I'm a bit ... '

He wishes she could see him, could see this phone call in its rightful context as the latest in a long line of things that are hard for him.

'Oh. Right.'

He begins to apologise, to try to explain himself.

'No, don't worry,' she says, her anger burning down the line. 'You just take care of yourself. Hope you're having a great fucking time at clown college.'

She hangs up. Tom removes the phone from his ear and throws it as hard as he can into the cushions of the cafe sofa. It makes an unsatisfyingly dull noise on impact, the screen black.

17

When they arrive at the Moroccan restaurant, Noémie and Wayne are already there, squabbling over something. They spot Tom and Billie threading themselves awkwardly between the tables to reach them, and Wayne gives a cheer of greeting that's almost inaudible over the music and the talk. They sit down, and Billie bends all the way left and then right to say hello, getting briefly confused by the number of cheek kisses.

'Is Matthias not coming?' Tom says.

'God no, this is very much not his vibe. Anyway, he's on the fifth day of a chemical foot peel so ...' Wayne doesn't finish this thought, and Billie is left with the image. He turns to her and beams.

'Bienvenue!' he says in a hammy French accent. 'Nice to see you again.'

Billie thinks it's good of him to act like they've really met, rather than been introduced in passing once when Billie ran into Tom in the street a few years ago.

'You are excited?' Noémie asks her in a way that is either accusatory or maybe just sounds that way because English isn't her first language. Billie splits her face into a smile and nods, which doesn't seem to completely satisfy Noémie. Tom and his friends break into an animated conversation about a co-worker of theirs, and Billie waits it out while studying the menu that she cannot read.

A waiter appears, and before Billie can ask Tom to translate some items for her, Noémie has ordered food for everyone and the menu is being pinched out of Billie's hands. Wayne adds a carafe of red wine for him and Noémie to share, Billie orders herself a beer and Tom does the same.

'Oh, he's drinking again!' Wayne says as he hands back his menu.

Billie notices a shifty look pass across Tom's face.

'Sometimes, yeah.'

'Thank God, you were so … flat, sober.'

Noémie makes a sound between a tut and a gasp and pretends to be about to hit Wayne with the back of her hand.

'Do what you want,' she says to Tom, and rounds on Wayne. 'And you, don't be a dickhead.'

'I'm kidding! No, I was kidding, really. I just mean usually people drink more after a terrible break-up so it was a bit like—' Wayne turns his hands up in a 'what the fuck' gesture.

Billie looks at Tom who is unfolding his napkin.

'It was terrible?' she asks.

Tom shakes his head and frowns a little in forced nonchalance, but stops when Wayne turns to put a comforting arm around him.

195

'Oh, God yes. Real Romeo and Juliet stuff. Well, not Romeo and Juliet because like, nobody's died.'

Something strangles in the air between them and Wayne opens his eyes wide.

'Oh my God, I really am being a dickhead, I'm so sorry.'

He reaches a hand across towards Billie and starts to laugh, deep and booming. She can't help but join him.

'It's fine.'

'Well, you know, onwards and upwards,' Tom says. 'I reckon we should share some of the meatballs as well if we're going to be walking around for hours.' He slaps his menu shut and shifts to look over the back of his chair for the waiter.

Billie looks at Tom's friends and wonders whether they also perceive this evasiveness, this way he has of slipping out through the back door of a conversation.

'You want to see the map?' asks Noémie, smoothly shifting the topic.

She reaches into her backpack and pulls out a plastic wallet containing several dog-eared A4 pages, shielding them a little with her body from the eyes of their fellow diners. She rifles through them and extracts the segment she's looking for, wipes some condensation from their glasses off the table with a forearm and puts the maps down. At first, Billie doesn't understand what she's looking at. There seem to be two maps, one in pale greys and greens and another on top of that, a wriggling mass of dark paths, covered in blue and orange notes. Noémie points at one looping line on the lower part of the paper.

'This is where we are now, at the surface level.'

Billie feels something like vertigo.

'They close up the entrances to the tunnels very often, so sometimes you go down in a—'

Noémie pauses and looks to Wayne.

'—what is it called, sewer plate?' She makes a flap-opening motion with her hand.

'Manhole cover,' Wayne provides.

'Yes manhole, you go down in those sometimes but then the police find them and make it impossible. So it is a challenge sometimes for people.'

Billie does not want to climb into a drain.

'So that's how we're going to get in?'

'No, it is impossible today those ways. There's a train tunnel with an entrance now.'

'Like a door?'

Noémie shrugs lightly.

'I don't know how it looks, we will look for it. Sometimes it's a door. It is one of the fun things that you have to explore to find the place to go down.'

'Cool. Kind of like parkour.' Billie doesn't know why she has set herself up to talk about work. Noémie's eyes very slightly uncouple from hers.

'No, it's not parkour,' Noémie says.

'No, I just meant the urban exploration element.'

'Parkour is not the same,' Noémie says, shuffling the maps back into their wallet and removing another layer to show them. She waits, the paper angled away from view as a waitress brings over their drinks and distributes them around the table. Billie tries to catch Tom's eye, to affiliate the two of them against this weird stranger, and then she remembers that Noémie is not a stranger to him. Billie looks back down at the map, at the spider crawl of its tiny black lines.

'It looks kind of scary.'

'You have claustrophobia,' Noémie says, and it's not a question.

Billie thinks of the man clinging to the floor of the Eiffel Tower.

'No, I don't think so. No, I think it'll be fun. I'm just, you know. Asking the questions.'

This seems to please Noémie and she nods a little.

'That's good, you have to take it a bit serious to go down.' She points at a speckled area of the map. 'This is where we will go tonight, *la plage.*'

Billie knows this much French.

'Why's it called the beach?'

'You will know why when we go there,' Noémie says, smiling.

Billie has a thought, and at the same moment she registers for the first time that Noémie is wearing full fisherman's waders. One rubber foot is peering out from under the table.

'How much water is in the tunnels?'

'Some places you can swim in it, but mostly we will find water only up to here,' says Noémie, indicating a point halfway up her thigh with the side of her hand. She casts an eye on Billie's clothes.

'You will be wet,' she says needlessly.

'So all these little open sections are like, what, caves?' says Tom, waving a finger over the map.

'Yes, rooms. Obviously we cannot go everywhere, it is like three hundred kilometres of tunnel.'

'No, I want to walk three hundred kilometres underground tonight please, Noémie,' Wayne says, which she ignores.

'There is a room shaped like a castle, but you have to crawl on your belly to go there and I think you don't want to crawl.'

Billie shakes her head. She does not want to crawl on her belly.

'And there is the Nazi bunker too but that is far and I don't like it there,' Noémie says, wrinkling her nose in distaste.

'There's a Nazi bunker? I thought the tunnels were used by the French Resistance,' says Tom.

Wayne hurries to swallow a mouthful of wine and looks at his watch before looking at Billie.

'This is when Noémie tells you that her grandparents fought in the French Resistance.'

'They did fight in la Résistance!' Noémie looks offended. Wayne laughs loudly and Billie finds herself swept along with it again.

'Everyone in France will tell you their grandparents were in the French Resistance. Which, okay, but like ... some of them were with the Nazis, weren't they,' he says to Billie.

Noémie makes a sneering face at him that breaks into a smile as their food arrives, a terracotta pot of chicken stew, a rounded heap of couscous and bread steaming in a basket. They talk about the food, and Billie gives an account to Wayne of what she has been doing in Paris, what Tom has and has not let her go and see. Wayne plays up to her assessment of herself as the victim of Tom's pretentions, which she enjoys.

'Oh yes,' Noémie says, 'we will need codenames. I have one already, Lapine. You need to make one.'

'Yours is rabbit?' Tom asks.

'I had big ears in high school. Now they are pushed back by a doctor but, yes.' She splays one hand out from each side of her head. Billie notices that she has small loops for earlobes where plugs had once been.

'Codenames, okay yes, I love,' Wayne says, straightening in his chair to put his mind to it.

'Are you serious? Is that necessary?' Billie asks, and receives a shrug.

'You don't know who is police. So yes, it's what we do.'

'I'm gonna be something really masc. Like Hank. Hank Henchman.' Wayne takes a triumphant spoonful of stew. 'Okay, that's mine.'

Tom looks around the room for inspiration.

'He's going to pick some Shakespeare character or whatever,' Billie says to Wayne, feeling a kinship with him mostly because he's not Noémie. Tom smirks.

'Fuck off.'

'You guys should do a little family affair vibe,' Wayne says.

'Venus and Serena,' Noémie offers, and Wayne clicks a finger at her to lock it in.

'Yes. Done.'

'I'm not going to introduce myself to someone as Serena Williams,' says Tom.

'Oh *mon dieu*, it does not matter. Probably no one will ask you. Only don't say, "Hello, I'm Tom Perrin, nice to meet you."' Here Noémie does an actually quite good approximation of Tom's voice.

'I want to be Serena anyway,' says Billie, to join in, but the joke makes her cringe.

200

Tom throws his hands up and then pushes himself out of his seat.

'Time to make *une grosse commission*.'

Noémie gives a weary, disgusted look. Billie turns to Wayne for an explanation as Tom walks away.

'Take a huge shit,' he says.

Billie smiles as she thinks for the first time in years of something Tom used to do when they were younger: fart luxuriantly and then break into a rendition of 'Where is the Love?' by the Black Eyed Peas, beginning at the line 'chemical gases filling lungs of little ones'. In the lull of conversation Tom leaves behind him, the loud clatter of the restaurant seeps back into Billie's attention. She thinks that it is nice to be out somewhere busy and fun, and in thinking this she reminds herself that her father is dead.

Noémie carries on.

'The names are part of the thing of going to the catacombs. Nobody is who they are above, nobody is a rich man or a poor man. Everyone the same.'

'Oh God, it's not a sex thing, is it? Matthias is convinced it's a sex thing,' says Wayne, looking tired.

Noémie tuts and gets back to her plate.

'So what brought you to Paris?' Billie asks Wayne, wishing she were better at making small talk sober.

'I followed a boy,' Wayne says, rolling his eyes at himself. 'I was feeling kind of directionless and then I met him and I was like, oh my God, it's what the universe wants, blah blah. If it hadn't worked out it would be psycho, but because it did, it's romantic, right?'

Billie smiles at him.

'Can I ask you something?' she says.

'Please.'

'Why did they break up? Tom and Nour.'

'I don't really know. He didn't want to talk about it,' Wayne says in a lower voice, putting a conspiratorial hand on her arm and looking up to check that Tom is still in the bathroom. 'I was going to ask you actually.'

Noémie is now texting, her thumbs jabbing with practised aggression at her phone. Wayne leans over slightly to look at the screen and decides not to involve himself.

'What was she like?' Billie asks, hearing the awkwardness in her phrasing, like she's discussing another dead person.

'Oh yeah, great. I'm not sure she liked me all that much, but you know, that can happen with me. I'm sure you can imagine,' Wayne says without bitterness.

Billie finds she can't actually imagine not liking Wayne, but he doesn't leave her a space into which an obligation to respond could grow.

'I think they were good together, though. He was sort of different in front of her.'

'Different how?'

'I don't know. Luminous.'

They both find their gaze drawn automatically towards the toilet door, still closed. Then Wayne laughs.

'For God's sake, listen to me. Luminous! All right, F. Scott Fitzgerald.'

Tom emerges from the toilet and begins inching his way back towards them. Billie's phone illuminates on the table. She reads the message from her mum.

His illness was my whole life, and one day I just couldn't live it any more xx

The walls are peppered with mirrors of different shapes, and Billie can't avoid seeing her own reflection. In six or seven places around the room she can see the face of someone who's out of her depth. She replies to her mum that she loves her, and puts her phone away.

18

Tom gets to come to the supermarket because he's too big for the kids' club. Billie is with the other people her age painting some shells or something else babyish, but he is in the supermarket and he will get to choose which ice creams they get. He feels refreshed in here. His eyes that were heavy from the sun cream are waking back up a little. The supermarket smells of plastic and a sort of cheese he doesn't think they have at home, but not in a bad way.

There are so many kinds of food in here, and everything has a name that's new to him. He says the words above the aisles under his breath, to hear them. *Lecheria. Galletas. Cerveza.* A boy he met in the pool yesterday told him that you have to say the 'z' like a 'th'. He hisses the sound to himself. *Cervethhha.* Then: *pithha*, to try it out. He's glad he doesn't have a lisp for real, but it must be good to have a lisp and be Spanish.

There is a bad feeling around his parents like a heat in the cool of the supermarket. He has to stay near but he doesn't have to stay right next to them, so he wanders away to see what he can discover in this strange new world. There's an aisle full of bright red meat where one of the supermarket people is slicing bits of ham off a whole animal's leg. He looks at it and thinks about whether his own leg looks like that under the skin. The fish and prawns laid out on the beds of ice are more exciting than they are at Morrisons, because they're Spanish fish and prawns.

He breaks into a run in a long aisle of rice and pasta and his flip-flops slap on the tiles, like a perfect high five every time. He runs his fingers over some wine bottles to make them clink. He's getting a little bored. It's time to look for the ice creams. They've got all the kinds you have at home, Magnums and Cornettos and that sort of thing, but he's seen people walking around with ice creams in the shape of Sonic the Hedgehog. Those are the ones he wants. Not only do they look awesome but he imagines they probably turn your tongue and lips blue, which will be a lot of fun because he can lie on the ground and pretend that he's died.

He's thinking about Sonic so he takes the aisle at the fastest run he can and shoots out the other end. His parents are standing a few aisles away over by some salad, and he sees immediately that things are wrong. His mum is speaking in her calm voice, and his dad is agitated, tensed and sharp in his body. Tom's stomach starts to hurt. There are people around but they're trying not to stare at them. He turns around to look closely at a display rack of batteries so that people won't think he belongs with his parents. He hears a snarl of anger from his dad. He starts to feel prickly and he turns around even though he doesn't want to. He knows what these poses usually mean is coming next, this feeling, but he's never seen his dad do it in public before, so he still feels it like electricity through his whole body as he watches his dad spit in his mum's face.

Everyone reacts at once. A man in a vest that shows his chest hair moves towards his dad, yelling in Spanish, and then shoves his dad into a shelf of bananas. His dad tells him to fuck off, his face bright red, and the man's muscles suddenly seem much bigger and more threatening. Tom runs towards them and screams stop at everybody, his voice sounding high and useless. A little girl with arm bands on starts to squeal. Two of the supermarket staff are here now too, speaking into walkie talkies. His mum is trying her calm-down tone on the other shoppers now, but she doesn't speak Spanish and it's not working. She is shaking, the edge of her sarong skirt giving it away.

Tom begins to cry hard. Women are leading their children away. The man with the muscles is joined by two others who have run over from the other side of the supermarket, and the man pushes his dad again, who shoves him back. Tom can't breathe. Everybody is shouting now, and his dad barges his way through the tills and explodes out into the street. The men start to follow him but Tom rushes to put himself in their way. He screams at the men to leave them alone. He just has to make it end now, so they can go back to their holiday. His mum manages to shake off the people trying to look after her and she walks fast towards Tom. She takes his hand and leads him away from the shop, in the opposite direction from the resort. They walk so quickly that Tom almost can't keep up with her. He can feel his own heart thumping in his chest and his mum trembling through their clammy hands. His mum says in a low voice over and over that they're fine, and it's over now, and he nods for her even though he knows it isn't true. They walk for a long time in silence until they reach another supermarket, which doesn't sell the Sonic ice creams.

A few weeks later, the holiday is over but school hasn't started again yet. Tom goes for a playdate with Sean, up the road. He tells Sean about the blue tongue thing and Sean thinks it sounds cool. They compare the skin under their watch straps, how pale it is compared to the rest of them. Tom's tan is better than Sean's, and Sean tries to make him smell the rich, damp skin under where his watch face had been. It's a good playdate. Sean's older brothers allow him and Sean to watch them punch a woman with a short skirt and huge, solid boobs on *Grand Theft Auto*. They have the volume turned down low so Sean's mum won't hear it from the kitchen and know what they're playing. They would get in a lot of trouble, and Sean's mum is large and frightening.

When it's time for him to go home for dinner, he tells Sean's mum he's allowed to walk home alone, and she laughs her loud, hard laugh and tells him to put his shoes on and wait for her by the door. Sean and his brothers are hanging around the bottom of the stairs looking like they're planning to do something bad while she's gone, even though she'll only be gone five minutes. Tom waves goodbye and tries to show in the way he walks next to Sean's mum that he is a polite young man who wouldn't play *Grand Theft Auto* in her house without permission.

Then he hears shouting from up the street. His whole body goes tight. It's only faint, but Sean's mum must also be able to hear it. His dad's voice is so loud and clear, you can hear it even from here, several doors away. Tom looks up at Sean's mum's face, but she doesn't look at him. She frowns slightly and shakes her head. Then she puts her hand on Tom's shoulder and turns him back around.

'You like chicken casserole?' she says in a voice that's too gentle.

Tom nods. He does. They keep walking, her hand still guiding him.

'Come and help the boys finish it for me.'

Tom nods again. They go back inside Sean's house, where Sean gives him a double high five for pulling off the impossible trick of getting his mum to extend the playdate.

This is how Tom finds out that everybody who lives on their street knows what must be happening inside their house, that the walls don't hold it in. He had been wrong. The problem is not that nobody knows what's happening, but that, mostly, people want to pretend that they don't.

19

They leave the restaurant late, having taken their time over another round of drinks to pass the hours until the streets are empty and they can enter the tunnels. Tom sees that there is a certain sloppiness to the way Billie is moving and makes a mental note. The four of them walk apart, weaving around people stood in the road, following Noémie's lead. There's a small but busy supermarket on the corner of five streets branching off a fountain. Noémie points at it with the end of her cigarette, which she holds with her thumb and first two fingers, facing it in towards her hand in a way that Tom thinks must make her palms smell musty. They follow her inside.

'How long are we gonna be down there?' Tom asks Noémie as she loads her arms up with share bags of paprika crisps.

'Some hours, and it's a lot of walking so don't be shy.'

Billie peruses the fridge.

'Shall we get wine?' she asks Tom.

'I reckon just some beers.'

'Beers it is.'

Tom feels too full from dinner to think about food properly, but picks himself a packet of Haribo gold bears for the sake of it.

They reconvene outside the shop, and Noémie reshuffles the contents of their backpacks, passing a large bag of tea lights to Billie to carry. Noémie looks lit up, livelier than Tom has ever seen her, which is perhaps not that surprising given that he normally sees her at work.

'Down we go!' she says, and marches off towards the main road. Wayne wiggles his eyebrows at Tom, and Tom remembers what it feels like to rush with excitement.

When they reach a bridge over some railway tracks, Noémie takes a sweep of the surroundings. Satisfied that they are not being observed, she begins to climb up and over the wall that drops down onto a steep verge at the side of the tracks. They each follow her, Billie next, giving her open beer to Wayne to hold and to pass over to her, then Wayne, and then Tom. There is a low burn in the pads of Tom's thumbs from holding hot plates all day as he grips the wall. They pick their way down.

'We walk along here until we get to a tunnel,' Noémie says.

'And if a train comes do we ... ?' Wayne says, whipping around as though expecting to find one bearing down on them.

'No trains. Not since thirty years.'

Tom looks down at the tracks, burrowing through the ground beneath the moss and grasses.

'It's called the little belt. You don't know about it because you are a tourist with your head up your ass all day.'

Wayne links arms with Noémie as they walk.

'Mean,' he says.

The walls that climb back up to the streets running either side of them are overgrown with weeds. There is a damp, vital smell of soil. Noémie tells them again that she isn't precisely sure where in the tunnel the entrance is, that this sort of information is hotly guarded by the people who come down here. A fox whips across their path, briefly illuminated and then invisible again.

As they walk towards the mouth of the tunnel, Noémie switches on her head lamp and a handheld torch that swings crazily across the ground in front of them. Tom reaches up to turn on his headlamp, and Billie fiddles with her bike lights until they stop flashing and shine continuous white. She finishes her can and crumples it. On hearing the sound, Noémie doubles back and takes the can from her.

'All garbage give to me, we don't leave it,' she says and tucks the can into an outside pocket of her bag before striding on to lead the group again. Tom turns his head towards Billie, whose hand is still open from holding the beer, and accidentally blinds her with his beam.

'Fuck off, that's really bright,' she says, shaking her head jerkily as if she's trying to reset her eyeballs.

The darkness closes around them as they press on into the tunnel. The air becomes warmer and clammier. From deep into the distance, Tom sees three light sources, wriggling in his sightlines. Noémie spots them at the same moment and stops dead, holding up her hand for them to do the same. She hovers.

'If they are police we need to run now,' she says in a low voice, not taking her eyes off the lights.

Tom thinks of Billie's too-large shoes.

'Run where?' Billie hisses, but Noémie touches her arm to make her quiet.

'It's too late anyway. If they are police, pretend all of you to be American, also Billie you will need to cry, okay?'

Billie looks as if she does not think this is okay, but then each of the lights in the distance flickers off in quick succession. Noémie sighs.

'Not police. They think we are police.'

They keep walking, and eventually Tom can see three young men dressed in what he might have guessed was hiking gear if he saw them somewhere else. They are lightly dusted with dirt. Noémie sizes them up, and greets them in French.

'*C'est ouvert?*'

The men, who haven't broken their gait, cast looks at each other and pass them by.

'Is it open?' Noémie tries again.

'I don't know, maybe,' one shouts back over his shoulder in heavily accented English.

Tom frowns but Noémie laughs and shrugs.

'They don't know us.'

Tom tries not to meet Billie's eye, and for the first time he wonders exactly how illegal it is to be down here.

Once they're beyond the earshot of the other group, Noémie says that the presence of the men is a useful clue anyway: the entrance must be further inside the tunnel.

'Why would we have to pretend to be Americans?' asks Wayne.

'It's annoying for the police to arrest Americans,' says Noémie.

'Do people get arrested a lot down here?' asks Tom, knowing already what the answer is.

'Every day,' she says, moving away from the group to shine her torch along the seam where the side of the tunnel meets its floor. Billie moves closer to Tom and swings her bag around her body to extract two beers. She holds one out to him. He shakes his head and she puts the second in the inside pocket of her jacket.

'What are we actually looking for?' Wayne asks Noémie in a voice that feels too loud for the darkness.

'I think a hole,' her answer comes echoing back, and Tom's chest tightens. He has been imagining some kind of service door, maybe a neglected set of steps.

They look around for half an hour without any joy, mostly in silence punctuated by an occasional performative sigh from Wayne. Tom begins to court the possibility that they won't find it after all, and begins to be glad that this is the way it's going.

And then they find it.

'Here!' Wayne shouts. Billie runs over and Tom trails behind, feeling a little tired and aware of how late it already is. He braces himself to see what they are in for. The 'hole' really is just a hole. A gap between two slabs of stone, probably wide enough to accommodate a small person with their hands on their hips, which is how Billie is standing to appraise it. She looks over at Tom, and he comes to stand next to her. She speaks in a soft voice.

'You're sure about this, are you?'

He's not. But they are here now, and people come down here all the time, supposedly. Shuffling into a hole in the ground to go and crawl around illegal subterranean tunnels which may or may not be full of water but where there would certainly be no phone signal strikes him as a strangely neutral prospect. He feels disconnected in some way from consequence.

Wayne takes his backpack off and makes a show of limbering up.

'Fuck it, you only live once, don't you,' he says, in a tone so light that Tom can't help but feel like a coward. Tom looks at Billie, waiting for her to crack and say they can go home. But she shrugs and starts to ease her backpack off her shoulders.

Noémie throws her bag into the opening, and it makes a muffled thud onto some unseen surface. Billie does the same. Noémie follows her bag, shimmying down the muddy opening as the rest of them train their headlamps on her. She lands beneath, and they guide Wayne into the hole, then Billie. Then Tom is standing alone in the railway tunnel, uncomfortably aware of the quiet. He lowers himself into the hole and feels the cold stone press into his palms and fingers. His feet feel their way down the sides of the opening until he hits the floor of what he can now see is another tunnel, slightly wider than the opening, that runs below and parallel to the train tunnel above. He, Noémie and Billie are able to stand with their legs extended and their backs bent in this low space, but Wayne is sat on his haunches. Tom reaches a hand up to check for his head torch and obscures its light briefly in doing so.

'Torches on always, okay?' Noémie says, adjusting the straps on her backpack.

Tom turns to shine his beam on Billie, who looks a little underwhelmed.

'Is this it? The catacombs?'

Noémie smiles at them as she folds the plastic sheets of map into her jacket.

'No, this is like the foyer. I go first and you follow.'

Noémie turns and leads them, bent double and backpacks scraping along the stone, further down this path until the ceiling rises above them, and a rough stone archway announces their arrival at the catacombs proper.

'Sorry but there is like ... oxygen down here, isn't there?' Wayne's voice sounds stifled.

Noémie laughs and walks through the archway and into the darkness of the tunnel branching off to their right.

'Yes there is oxygen. You are breathing now, yes?'

Wayne takes three exaggerated breaths in a row as he follows Noémie, bending his head slightly to keep it from meeting the rock above them.

20

Billie scrolls through Mary-Jean's Instagram posts on the bus. Three yellow labradors bounding into a lake. Her dad and Mary-Jean on the dance floor at someone else's wedding with a filter on the photograph that blurs out the background. Three disembodied hands clinking glasses with the caption 'Music, wine and friends ... cheers!'. Mary-Jean in Dublin with a group of women, each in a pair of wraparound sunglasses wearing T-shirts that read 'I leprechan't even'. What must be her dad and Mary-Jean's enormous front room, decked out for some kind of party. Billie splays two fingers on the screen to zoom into the photos displayed on their mantelpiece, but she can't tell who they're of.

This route takes her through parts of London she's hardly ever been to before, quiet-looking bits of south west London that don't have a tube stop, and then into a queue of traffic snaking over the river. She gets off the bus, holding a wrinkled quiche flat in front of her like a waitress at a cocktail party. She checks the address again one handed, and goes over names in her head. Mary-Jean's sister Louise, whose kids are both J something . . . Joy and James? Jimmy? It's all flower boxes and black railings around here, shiny cars.

She reaches Louise's front door and presses the doorbell, which sings a flimsy tune into the house. Her hands prickle under the still-cooling quiche and she's too hot in her clothes. She listens to someone clacking over a wooden floor towards her, and the door swings open.

'Hiiiii! Happy Thanksgiving!' says Mary-Jean, pulling Billie into a hug, shoulders first to protect her dress, bright blue with a collar that is open to reveal a large square necklace in some kind of brown stone.

'Happy Thanksgiving!' Billie replies, trying to match Mary-Jean's enthusiasm. She tries not to drop the quiche as she unbuttons her coat with one hand and pulls off her scarf in the uncomfortable warmth of the house.

'Well look at you!' Mary-Jean makes a show of assessing Billie's outfit. 'Love it!'

'Thanks,' says Billie, not knowing what there might be to love about her jumper and jeans, which were all that had been clean that morning.

'Did you love the doorbell? We thought it would be fun to reprogram it, they had that or "Happy Birthday" so we thought, why not. It's fun, right?'

'Oh, yeah,' she says, as Mary-Jean takes the crook of her arm and leads her into a tidy, white living room.

'"The Yellow Rose of Texas"? You know it?'

Billie shakes her head apologetically, and Mary-Jean gasps.

'Oh lord, well it looks like we've got some musical education to do today!'

217

The living room is connected to another room through a narrow passageway, and Billie can hear screams coming from somewhere beyond that. Mary-Jean surveys the fire in the grate, and then relieves Billie of her quiche.

'Wonderful, thank you so much, okay great, I'm gonna take this on through, the restroom's off the hall upstairs if you want to freshen up,' says Mary-Jean, in a tone that isn't quite a question, and marches off towards the screams. Billie stands alone next to the fireplace for a moment and then goes upstairs to the bathroom, where the mirror shows her the faint streak of Nutella on her left temple. She wipes it off, and then realises that she is wearing a red and white striped top with blue jeans and that Mary-Jean thinks she has come in some kind of misguided attempt at American national dress.

As Billie is coming out of the bathroom, a small boy jumps out at her. She makes an undignified noise in surprise.

'I got you!' the boy yells, laughing maniacally.

'You did.'

'You're Billie,' he tells her, 'I know already.'

She had expected them to have American accents, but they must have lived here a long time. She begins to reply but he doesn't leave her room to.

'I'm Jonathan,' he says, holding out a hand to shake.

'Hi, Jonathan,' she says, as the boy shakes her hand with both of his, like a football manager welcoming a new trans-fer, before thundering away down the stairs. She stands confused, having never received a handshake from an eight-year-old before, and then follows him, wondering what kind of subtle psychological scarring it must cause a little boy to be named Jonathan.

Beyond the living room there is a huge, echoey kitchen and dining room, where she finds Mary-Jean and a woman who sounds like her discussing whether to take something out of the oven. Through a wall of glass doors, she can see that Jonathan and Joy are filming some snails on one of the garden walls with an iPad.

And there is her dad, distributing wine glasses over a table. He looks ruffled, wearing an apron with a dishtowel stuffed into the front pocket, but he's in high spirits. He puts down the glasses and edges himself out from behind the table towards her. He comes in for a hug, making an exaggerated sigh of exhaustion.

'Almost there now, hello, hi, sweetheart.'

Billie hugs him back, feeling observed even though Mary-Jean and Louise are still assessing a bright orange pie through the oven door, Louise with a hand on Mary-Jean's back as she crouches. He gives her one tighter squeeze before releasing her.

'Smells good,' Billie says, hovering closer to the kitchen island to greet Louise and tell her how nice it is to be here, what a wonderful home she has, could she help with anything. Louise turns heavily and catches sight of her.

'*So* rude of me, I am sorry, hello there, it's so good to meet you!' Louise, a squatter, harder-featured version of Mary-Jean, inches towards Billie. She reaches both arms up and holds Billie's shoulders to get a better look at her.

'Very like you, William,' she says over Billie's shoulder. 'The spit! And such a cute outfit, oh my goodness.'

Billie remembers being on a bus once with her dad and a couple of American tourists, and her dad saying very loudly that Americans can't help remarking on everything they see, like dogs would if they could talk.

'Now, we're running a little late, so I hope you're not too hungry,' says Mary-Jean, shooing Louise to go and take a seat in an armchair by the window. 'And she's not supposed to be moving around, don't let Little Miss Independent tell you different.'

Louise makes a scrunched face at her sister. Billie recalls that the reason they're here for Thanksgiving instead of in Cleveland is because Louise needed a hysterectomy and isn't yet well enough to travel.

'How are you feeling?' Billie asks.

'Good! Good actually. Well, not *good* but—' Louise eases herself into the chair, and groans softly, leaving her sentence unfinished.

'Can I get you something?'

'Sure, I'll have a beer, and get one for yourself,' she says, gesturing to the fridge with a nod of her head. Billie opens the door and spots something covered in miniature marshmallows. Joy darts in under her arm, thrusts her fingers in a bowl of sauce and darts away again, too quick for Billie to say hello.

'I've never had a Thanksgiving before,' Billie says as she passes beers out to her dad, knowing that they will already know this.

'Well don't you worry, your dad's only got one year on you,' says Mary-Jean, squeezing her arm on the way to add another pie to the already quite numerous pies on the countertop. Billie remembers another of Mary-Jean's Instagram posts, from this time last year, of her dad pulling a wishbone with Mary-Jean, all of their teeth showing in delight.

'You've *never* had Thanksgiving dinner?' asks Joy, running back into the room with some conspicuous sticky fingerprints on the hem of her dress.

'Nope, never.'

Joy gives her a look of open-mouthed horror. 'You've never had a turkey?'

'Well, I've eaten turkey before, just not on Thanksgiving.'

Joy shakes her head in a way that indicates that this isn't the same, then loses interest in the conversation and runs off.

'Mary-Jean, please, give me something to do.'

'Honey I hardly know who Mary-Jean is, call me MJ. Like Michael Jackson!' Mary-Jean gives an approximation of a moonwalk that she seems to find hilarious and Billie feels a sharp thrill of embarrassment.

'Is she moonwalking?' Louise calls from her armchair as Mary-Jean doubles over, hooting with laughter. Billie's dad comes up from the basement, each of his large hands around the neck of a wine bottle.

'You can keep the little monkeys away from the food, how does that sound?' Mary-Jean says.

Soon, Billie has been treated to all of Joy's favourite songs from the *Moana* soundtrack, with detailed descriptions of what happens in the film at the moment each song appears, and her dad has played several rounds of a Formula One video game with Jonathan. She watches her dad instead of the screen. She scrutinises his reaction to Jonathan's yells, and to being asked to fetch and carry things between races. It strikes her that she probably won't get a chance to talk to him properly unless he makes that time now. He doesn't seem to be thinking about this.

Two months earlier, Billie had received a phone call from him, saying that he and Mary-Jean would be back in the UK over Thanksgiving weekend. His voice had sounded deep and soft, and he had described seeing a new doctor, being on new medication, turning new corners in every area of his life. She had smiled down the phone and said it was great. It was great. She wanted very much for it to be great. She looks at him today and she can't tell to what extent he actually does seem different, and to what extent that is wishful thinking. Physically, something does seem to have changed. She thinks he may have dyed his hair a little darker, or done something else that means he looks less balding than he used to. His face seems a slightly different shape, or shade. Maybe he's thinner. He sends her emails sometimes with pictures of him and Mary-Jean looking hale and happy in outdoorsy clothing. But she can't say whether the change runs any deeper. This is a person she doesn't know very well yet. America Dad.

The food is ready, and they sit down around it, the turkey glistening next to piles of beige and brown food steaming softly. Jonathan, next to her, reaches out a hand and mimes grabbing fistfuls of the marshmallows, which Joy informed her are hiding some mashed sweet potatoes, and shovelling them into his mouth, bouncing in his chair with excitement. They all start to scoop and slice and ladle themselves a plate. When Mary-Jean leans forward to pick up the gravy boat, Billie realises that the thing the large brown necklace is reminding her of is the barrel of brandy on a St Bernard.

Once everything is served, Louise clears her throat and addresses the table. Billie looks at her plate and hopes she's not going to have to wait until the food is cold to eat it.

'All right so, the clue's in the name folks, let's give some thanks!' she says. 'Let's go anticlockwise, just for the hell of it.'

Billie sees Joy trace a few semicircles in the air with her finger to confirm which direction that is. Jonathan gives Billie a sly jab in the ribs and leans in to stage whisper:

'You have to give thanks for something you're thankful for.'

'Thank you,' she says in a stage whisper of her own.

'And that doesn't count!' Jonathan says, pointing an accusing finger at her, visibly delighted at his own joke.

'Okay, me first then,' Mary-Jean says, putting her hands together in a practised motion. 'I am thankful this year for family, old and new.' She directs this last part at William, touching his arm, and then beams at Billie, who smiles back sheepishly. Louise goes next.

'Well, I hope it's not too corny to say I'm thankful for my health,' she says, for which Mary-Jean gives her an arm squeeze too, and Joy does a firm series of nods to show her approval.

'You're up, honey,' Mary-Jean says to Joy, who stands on her chair to deliver her thanks in a ceremonial tone.

'I am thankful for . . . joy!' she says, and bursts into laughter and flops back into her chair.

'She says that one every year,' Jonathan tells Billie.

'That's because it's true!' Joy screams at her brother in full voice, and all the adults shush her gently.

'And our newbie?' says Louise, and Billie wishes she'd been warned about this more than a minute ago.

'I'm thankful for . . . oh, getting a job. Well, it's an internship. But you know.' Billie raises her glass half-heartedly. 'For having something to do.'

223

Her dad gives her an approving wink, which is not a gesture she associates with him at all.

'Ahem!' shouts Jonathan. 'I would like to announce that I am thankful for my PlayStation 4.'

His three relatives protest and he throws up his hands in defeat.

'Okay okay! Fine. I am thankful I'm happy and healthy and blah blah, blah blah blah.' He folds his arms.

'That will have to do,' says Louise. 'William, round us off.'

Billie's dad looks around at them all and curls his fingers over Mary-Jean's hand, resting next to his plate.

'This year I am grateful—'

'THANKFUL,' Jonathan shouts, and Louise shushes him.

'Of course, yes, sorry, I am *thankful*. Very thankful indeed, for second chances.'

Mary-Jean gives him a huge smile, and he looks down into his plate and then up at Billie. She meets his gaze and feels a swell of discomfort she can't quite name.

'Lovely, everybody,' Mary-Jean tells them. 'Okay, off we go!'

They start to eat. Billie is glad that she can play up to the new and exciting food for conversation, but some small talk is still inevitable.

'How's the work going?' her dad asks her across the table, although he already knows how it's going because they emailed about it last week. They are performing parts for the rest of the table.

'Oh, yeah. Good. I mean it's only the first month so, difficult to say. Settling in still and stuff.'

'What do you do?' asks Louise.

'I don't know whether it's like, "what I do" or anything,

224

more like what I'm doing right now, if you know what I mean. It's public relations?'

'Oh right, yep,' Louise nods. 'Well, hey, you're twenty-two, right? It doesn't matter what you do right now. Do whatever!'

Billie nods. This is the kind of thing people Louise's age say to her.

'And your brother, what's his name?' she asks.

'Tom? He's an actor, sort of. I guess not at the moment, actually. He lives in Paris.'

'Oh yes yes, very nice,' says Louise, breezing over this answer. 'Well, that's a shame, or we could have met him today!'

Billie nods again and avoids her dad's eye. Jonathan chooses this moment to demand a review from everybody at the table of his napkin drawing in gravy of what he insists is a dog.

Her dad talks about his school, the ongoing rehearsals for some kind of winter show he is helping with, and Joy very quietly and soberly sings them a verse of *Jingle Bells* with her eyes closed, to rapturous applause. They each work their way through a dusty orange slice of pumpkin pie, about which Mary-Jean makes a Trump joke in a way that Billie thinks is designed to prove that she's not the bad kind of American. The afternoon wears into evening. Her assessment, by the end of the meal, is that her dad is being one of the best versions of himself, but even though she hoped that this is what she'd find, it makes her feel strangely empty. She feels old and adrift, sat at this table with this family that is not hers.

After a heated debate and one short burst of tears from Joy, the two children decide that the movie they want to watch after the meal is *The Polar Express*. Her dad gives Billie an over-egged eye-roll.

225

'We watched it last night too.'

Billie smiles. It's her cue to leave. Mary-Jean and her dad go into the other room to feed the fire, and Billie helps to clear some plates, ferrying things to the dishwasher while the children scrape food in and around the bin.

'You really must take some leftovers with you, save us from ourselves,' says Louise.

'No!' Jonathan yells, and throws his little body in front of the pumpkin pie as though protecting it from gunfire.

'Don't be so rude, Jonathan, you would be glad to share your pie.'

Billie looks at Jonathan, whose face suggests he would not be very glad at all.

'So where will you be for Christmas?' Louise asks her.

'We used to stay in London—'

A sharp, deep bark of rage reaches them from the other room, followed by shushing. The children stop scraping to look at each other, then at their mother, and finally at Billie. Her face flushes and she goes back to focusing on the plates, her heart racing with an old panic.

'—but yeah. Now we go to Glasgow, near Glasgow, with my – my aunt and my mum live there.'

Mary-Jean bustles back into the room and beams at them all, colour high in her cheeks. She beckons for Joy and Jonathan to come and join her.

'Okay, you two, *The Polar Express* awaits!'

They trail her back through into the other room, holding themselves warily. Billie and Louise are left alone. Billie keeps loading dishes, willing her pulse to slow down, and perceives that Louise is weighing up whether to say something.

226

'Listen—'

Billie wishes keenly that she was at home. Louise continues in a lowered voice.

'—I'm sorry if this is . . . I mean, it is a little inappropriate. But she's my only sister and I feel protective of her, especially since she's over there and I'm over here.'

Billie keeps her gaze on the plates.

'So, yes. I feel I have to ask you whether I should be worried. About your dad. His . . . '

She trails off. Billie feels she has to meet her eye now, and when she does, she sees someone who is afraid. Billie's throat is tight as she searches for a precedent for this situation and finds none. The silence continues and then Louise buckles.

'I'm so sorry, I shouldn't be—'

'Maybe,' says Billie, in a voice just large enough for Louise to hear. Louise looks at her as though she wants to ask more and then decides against it.

'Okay. Okay, thank you.'

Louise gives her shoulder a conciliatory rub and Billie feels dead.

'You'll take some of this food with you, won't you? You have roommates, right?'

Billie nods, and Louise hands her a canvas tote out of a cupboard, some Tupperware out of a drawer and directs her towards each of the leftovers in turn. Billie loads herself up as quickly as she can without looking like she's hurrying, and doesn't manage to avoid Louise pulling her into a hug that lasts slightly too long.

Once she's buttoned up in her coat, she puts her head around the door to announce her departure to the others.

Mary-Jean kisses her own hands repeatedly and blows them at Billie, and then prompts the kids, who mumble a goodbye without quite looking away from the film. Billie's dad shuffles himself up from the sofa and follows her into the corridor.

'Really good to see you, sweetheart,' he says. 'Let's be sure to see each other again before I leave.' Whatever had agitated him earlier has passed through him now. His eyes are soft.

'I'd like that,' she says.

'Ah,' he says, putting a finger up in remembrance of something. He disappears back into the house, and then returns with two identical presents, wrapped up beautifully with a ribbon and deep green paper. 'For you and Tom. For Christmas.'

'Oh. Thank you,' she says, placing them in the tote on top of the leftovers. She hadn't thought to bring him something, and decides to postpone crying about this until later on.

As she walks down the front path, Mary-Jean's heels clack towards the doorway. The gate shrieks shut behind her, and she looks back to see that her dad and Mary-Jean are waving widely, even though they're only a few feet away.

'Safe journey, sweetheart!' says Mary-Jean, and then the door encloses them. Billie is already on the bus when she remembers about the tray she brought the quiche in, the only one she owns.

21

They walk in single file, the roof of the passage ribbed by the shadows their head torches cast. There is an overlapping patchwork of graffiti on the walls, very new and very old-looking sections hugging close to one another. Billie turns to shine her light on some lettering chiselled into the stone.

'Are these street names?' she says.

'Yes, they match above,' Noémie calls back, her voice bouncing around in the tunnel. They walk in what is, for Billie at least, nervous silence, until they reach the first fork in the road. They huddle at the intersection, trying not to blind each other with their torches.

'All good?' Noémie asks, and the other three nod back.

'Which way?' Tom asks, peering around them to illuminate each pathway. Noémie confirms with the map.

'Right. Left goes to a *chatière* and you won't like it.'

'A . . . catflap,' Wayne translates.

'Yes, it is the name for a hole you crawl through to get to the next tunnel. Okay, we go.'

Noémie sets off right, and Billie tries to think about something other than shuffling her body through a pitch-black hole in the ground. A large and athletic-looking spider makes a crackle of movement on the wall.

They walk, ducking beneath low ceilings and sloshing through puddles of cloudy water, listening to the sounds of their own footfall and the tinny pop music Wayne is playing from his phone. Billie feels the beer and the rhythm of their march dulling the edge of her anxiety, but it rushes back when she turns her head to meet oncoming tunnels, spurs of pathway that lead off past dusty piles of rock and ancient iron grates into unseen parts of the network. She focuses on Tom's back directly ahead of her. At the top of his head as it begins to slope towards her, she can see a lighter swatch of scalp beginning to make itself known through the hair. She wonders whether he knows about it, and feels vaguely uncomfortable with this evidence that he is getting older.

They walk for what feels like a long time, and Billie finds their progress more and more meditative, not so different from a walk on the surface. Then they pass an alcove with a pair of cowboy boots glued to its roof, and littered with fragments of what is unmistakably human skeleton.

'You said no fucking bones,' Billie says loudly, the sudden volume of her voice making the other three flinch.

Tom twists around to smile at her apologetically and scrapes his bag along the wall, releasing a shower of dust and pebbles.

'Be careful of the tunnel.' Noémie spins around to admonish him. 'And yes there are bones, *bien sûr*. It's not a problem.'

Billie decides that she doesn't like Noémie very much.

She takes a picture of the boots, and when the flash goes off brightly she expects some sort of reproach from Noémie about photography being prohibited, but she doesn't say anything.

Eventually, they pass through a cave carved out to look like a barbecue pit, with a large and poor likeness of Vincent Vega on the wall in spray paint. There are other people here. A young man wearing a synthesiser modified to sit around his torso like a waistcoat is giving a deeply earnest performance of a piece of music with a heavy, slowing beat, like a heart at the end of its life. Three people are watching, all wearing hiking gear like the men they saw on the train tracks, who give Billie and her party a glance and a nod before turning back to the synthesiser with solemn attention. The four of them stand there and join in the watching for a few minutes, the opening of a can occasionally interrupting the music, and Billie reflects on the large number of ways there are for people to be insane. The performer reaches the end of his piece with a flourish, and bows to thunderous applause and cheers. The small crowd gestures that they should join them in the pit. Noémie speaks to them, and Billie assumes that she is explaining their intention to head further in. The sharp, body odour smell of a joint reaches her.

As they move deeper inside the network, they begin to find passages submerged under a layer of water. Billie braces herself for the icy slip of liquid into her shoes, but it is luke-warm. When she turns her torch towards it, it's opaque and beige grey like an abandoned cup of tea.

'It's only rain, nothing gross,' Noémie calls over the splash of their footfall.

Billie feels the water climb up her leggings and clam to the skin at the back of her knees. They pass an opening directly above them, and she shines her torch up into the ragged cavity.

'Is this a manhole?'

'Yes, but an old one if there is no ladder?' Noémie replies.

There is no ladder, only rock. It reminds Billie of endoscopy footage. A new awareness that she is the last one in the group, and that there is only open tunnel behind, overwhelms her. Spinning around to be sure, she notes with a swoop of dread that the beam of her headlamp only lights up the first ten metres or so, after which point the darkness swallows it completely. She continues to take pictures here and there of bits of graffiti and strange carvings in the rock as they walk, and documenting the tunnels like this gives her a slight but still comforting feeling of being in control.

Her feet are aching by the time they round a corner and Noémie turns to them with her arms raised in celebration.

'*Bienvenue à la plage,*' she says as they look around at the cavern they find themselves in. It's one of the larger spaces they have passed through, but still Billie finds that she had been imagining something more like an actual beach. It's a wide cave with benches made of stacked bricks on three sides, above which the ceiling is covered with scribbled tags in white paint. Taking up the entire back wall is a squatter, cruder version of a painting of a wave she's seen many times before somewhere, with a little brown boat climbing its curve. To their right, a graffiti volcano rises up out of the rock, billowing clouds up into the shadows. She notices that there are little indentations in the walls and beer cans with one side cut out of them hanging from the ceiling.

'Billie, you have the candles?'

Billie takes the plastic bag out of her backpack, giving a handful to each of them. They spread out around the cave, positioning tea lights anywhere they will sit level, the glow expanding as each one is lit. In this new light, the cave looks cosier and more welcoming.

Faintly, the sound of dance music and yelling reaches them from some other part of the tunnel network.

'Sometimes there are many other people down here, but sometimes you don't see anybody,' Noémie says, coming over to collect more tea lights. 'You have to be friendly, okay?'

She directs this at Billie personally, who nods and feels offended. The beers in her bag are still a little cold from the corner shop fridge. Billie opens one and hears it echo around the cavern. She sits down. The music is definitely coming closer to them now.

Noémie lifts cans out of her bag and lines them up against the wall where they can lean on the cold stone. Billie hears a rattling sound and sees some beads snaking over the backs of Noémie's hands before she stuffs them back into the rucksack and zips it shut.

'Is that a rosary?'

'You never know,' she says.

Once they've all sat down, opened a drink and been given a Prince biscuit each by Wayne, a brief silence settles.

'If I wanted to hang around in a smelly basement I would have stayed at work,' says Wayne.

Noémie gives him a kick, but it's an affectionate one. Being down here has put her in a happy mood, and she looks around with pride. Wayne puts his music back on, loud enough to compete with the other noise.

'Why do you guys work there?' Billie asks.

Wayne gives a long, groaning sigh.

'Oh, it's not that bad. The hours fit around my masters and they like native English speakers for the whole ye olde pub vibe.'

Billie looks at Noémie who interprets her next question.

'For me, my friend used to work there and said it's easy to steal from the till.'

Wayne and Tom laugh. Billie joins them.

'Oh, she's not joking,' Wayne clarifies.

Noémie flashes the corner of some notes at Billie from the top of her jeans pocket. She shrugs.

'It's a chain and the manager is thick like a pig.'

Billie denies Noémie the satisfaction of seeming impressed by her thieving and turns to Wayne instead.

'Is it an acting masters?'

'God no, child psychology,' he says. 'No, the whole acting world got a bit much. Like I would find myself in a workshop pretending to incubate an alien foetus in my mouth while the rest of the class threw me a baby shower and be like, what the fuck am I doing?'

He laughs.

'And it was like, why am I working part time in a call centre selling wine subscription packages so I can audition to play another fucking doctor or IT guy. So yeah, now I'm all about children's brains.'

He takes a drag of his cigarette.

'Why are you in PR then?' he asks.

'Because they were the ones who offered me the job. The internship.'

She perceives Tom filter his interest back into their conversation.

'It's advertising, right?' says Wayne.

'Yeah basically,' Tom answers for her.

She bristles.

'It's not actually advertising, but there wouldn't be anything wrong with that if it was,' she says looking at Wayne but speaking to Tom.

'Did I say there was?' Tom says, a look of feigned confusion on his face.

Billie continues speaking to Wayne.

'I just wanted to get moving I guess, get started on life.'

'Cool.' Wayne nods as he considers this. 'God that's nice, I feel like I never meet people who are excited by life any more.'

'Right. I mean, that's not really what I meant. Kind of the opposite actually. More like, life is hard and scary so you can't just fuck around and hope for the best.'

She knows that Tom will feel that this is directed at him, and doesn't especially mind.

'Oof.' Wayne turns to Tom. 'Well that's us told.'

Billie flushes and tries to backpedal.

'No no, sorry that came out like—'

'No look you're probably right. Who the fuck knows. Who cares!'

Wayne lifts his can into the air as though toasting the idea. Billie wonders whether it's odd that she does care, but her thoughts are interrupted because the sound of music from elsewhere in the tunnels is very loud now.

The four of them trail off their conversations as they wait

for the source to appear. Billie begins to be able to identify the track.

'Is that Skrillex?'

Wayne rolls his eyes. 'Don't, French people have the worst taste in music. Matthias listens to such shit.'

They are joined by a group of five teenagers, who spill into the room falling over each other and laughing. They're dressed mostly in black and Billie thinks that 'emo' is probably no longer the right word to describe them, but it's the one that comes to mind. There are two girls, one very tall and gawky with vibrantly orange eyeliner, and one smaller and stockier with a buzzcut. Two of the boys seem to fit together, jostling each other with a goofy affinity, one with a neck tattoo, the other with long hair dangling out from beneath a beanie. The third boy seems reluctant to be there and much less coolly dressed than the others, which clicks into place for Billie when he takes the tall girl's hands in his own. Noticing that they're all wearing what seem to be their normal clothes, Billie feels superior to Noémie in her waders. The teens turn their music down a little when they see that they're not alone, and Noémie rises to greet them. She offers them cans of beer in a perfunctory way, and they refuse them in the same manner, as though these are merely motions they have to go through. Billie tilts her head subtly in order to read the neck tattoo. She thinks it might say 'requiem'.

Billie stiffens with nerves as they sit down close to their group, and engage Noémie and Tom in their own conversation. Although she only met Wayne and Noémie a few hours ago, now they feel like people she knows and trusts in the face of total strangers. She recalls Noémie's remark at dinner that people can be anybody and do anything down here. This no longer seems like a good thing.

'Okay, a smelly basement with shit music, so now it's *exactly* like work,' says Wayne quietly, wrinkling his nose at the noise. Billie laughs. She has to try to enjoy this.

She works her way through her beers and treads water at the edges of the conversations for a while, feeling herself detaching as they switch between speaking in French and re-hashing old in jokes from the pub. Tom apparently once absent-mindedly asked Noémie to get him a Dairy Milk from the shop and she came back with two litres of semi-skimmed, which Wayne and Tom seem to think is the funniest thing in the world. The teenagers move in and out of talking to them, talking near them, and showing each other little dance steps and collapsing into hysterics about them. Eventually Billie feels she ought to try to reinsert herself, and so she asks Noémie whether anything has changed in the tunnels since she started coming down here. Noémie nods and straightens up in a way that makes Billie think she likes giving her opinions on this topic.

'It's not how it was when I was young. Airbnb let people have a sleepover here a few years ago for a competition. With breakfast and bed and all this bullshit.'

'You are such a grandmother, listen to yourself,' says Wayne. 'Back when you were a nipper people left their doors on the latch, did they?'

'I don't know what is nippers and latch, but be quiet.' She swigs from her can and turns back to Billie. 'It was so nice to go underground, when we were younger. You leave bad things above,' she points to the ceiling and Billie remembers there are thousands of tonnes of rock and buildings above her head, 'and bring only good things down to here. So yes, it's special to me.'

'God, I never did anything cool or daring when I was little,' says Wayne. 'I was such an only child. I used to curate a museum of my favourite objects in my bedroom and force my parents into guided tours of it.'

'I was not so young. I was maybe fourteen the first time I came down.'

'Okay we're not gonna get into how old I was when I did the museum.'

'There are secret things under every city. London probably also,' says Noémie.

Billie thinks. 'We had the fatberg, I suppose. I wouldn't want to go and hang out with it, though.'

'*C'est quoi* fatberg?' Noémie asks Wayne, who laughs instead of replying. Then his face lights up.

'Oh, I know what we should do,' he says, looking around at the three of them with mischief in his eyes. 'Ghost stories!'

Noémie smiles a dark smile.

'I don't think you want to hear the ones I know down here.'

'I don't really get ghost stories,' Tom says. 'I guess I think the things people do in real life are much scarier.'

Wayne does an enormous eye roll and groans into a laugh.

'Oh my God that's the kind of like, fake deep thing they use as a tagline for airport thrillers.'

Billie enjoys this and laughs loudly.

'It'll be fun, come on, get into it,' says Wayne. Tom claps his hands together to show his willing, and gets up to grab another couple of beers while Wayne gestures for Noémie and Billie to gather closer. Wayne fumbles in his bag for his torch, and lights his face from below, adjusting it slightly and looking to Billie for confirmation of which position makes him look spookiest. The shadow of his skull is cast enormous on the ceiling. The tall girl gets Noémie's attention to ask her a question in French, and becomes excited when Noémie answers yes, slapping her friends on the arms to come and join the circle. They all shuffle around to make room. The less coolly dressed boy puts a proprietorial arm around his girlfriend, who has both hands on her heart in pre-emptive fear.

'Okay, I get to start because it was my idea,' says Wayne, putting on a managerial sort of voice. The boy in the beanie gestures for him to wait, and scrambles to his feet. He dashes around the space, blowing out most of the candles. Billie feels a creeping sensation as the dark lowers on them. Wayne waits for a hush to fall, and lets the silence steep a little before he begins.

'I used to go running a lot around my old neighbourhood in London. I worked out this perfect 5k loop that would take me through the park, and then back home again without too many main roads. And there was this one road on the route that was quieter than the others.'

The tall girl is whispering a simultaneous translation to her boyfriend, and the sound adds an undercurrent that makes Billie's hair stand up on the back of her neck. Wayne gives the girl a look that implies that he feels this is ruining the performance, though, and she stops.

'And whenever I ran down that road, I never saw anybody, but I would start to feel strange. Like someone was watching me. Sometimes, I thought I could hear someone else's feet running just out of step with my own.'

The boy with the neck tattoo lets out a noise of anticipation, and is shushed by his friends. The darkness feels more and more pressing.

'I didn't think too much of it, and it was the only route that it made sense to run near my house. It was the best route to the park. So I thought, you know, maybe it's something happening physically with my body, with the blood in my ears after I've run a certain distance. But it happened every time. The sounds of footsteps, and sometimes even ... breathing.'

The girl with the buzzcut, eyes wide, whispers '*putain*' to herself.

'But then one day, as I was coming to the end of that road, I saw a friend of mine crossing at the top of it. So I waved, and she waved back, and I carried on jogging towards her while she stood and watched me. But she had this confused look on her face. And when I reached her, she kept looking beyond me, and eventually she said ... '

There is total silence.

' ... who was that man running with you?'

Billie's stomach drops and the teenagers all let out screams that sound incredibly loud in the cavern. Wayne glows with satisfaction.

'But when I turned, there was nobody there.'

There is a general hubbub of agreement that this is indeed a scary story. The guy with the neck tattoo puts his hand up to speak and then snatches it down again.

'I can tell a story?'

They all nod and he reaches for the torch and illuminates

his face, at which his friends all make a low 'ooooh' to set the scene.

'This,' he says in a voice much deeper and more resonant than the one he has been using so far, 'is a story . . . of the little girl's hand from a ghost.'

His friend in the beanie interrupts him in loud, rapid French and slaps the arm of his jacket hard with the back of a hand. This sends the neck tattoo guy into hysterics, and the friend takes over. The story is not, apparently, about a little girl's hand, but a little girl who sees a hand with no fingernails hovering around whenever bad things happen. He tells it in a mixture of broken English and French, and Billie doesn't understand the ending, but thinks it involves the little girl losing her own fingernails. It doesn't have the same impact as Wayne's story, and the girl with the buzzcut pats the boy's leg in a conciliatory way once he's finished. Billie feels suddenly and acutely lonely.

'Billie, you tell one,' says Tom. 'I don't think I have any.'

She has been racking her brains for a contribution but has also come up with nothing. She had a ghost story she used to tell as a pre-teen, about a time she was walking through a cemetery at night and had seen a figure all in white staggering around, but a friend had interrupted her telling it once to point out that the cemetery was right next to a student halls of residence and it was probably someone very drunk in fancy dress.

'Okay. I have a story . . . ' Noémie milks the pause, 'about the catacombs.'

The boys yell their approval as the two girls shake their heads with dread, and the teenagers all grip each other and

241

shuffle themselves into new listening positions. Billie feels sure that she does not want to hear this story. She looks over at Wayne and Tom who look too eager for her to object. Wayne offers Noémie the torch, but she declines in a way that suggests she knows her story is scary enough without special effects. Billie cracks another can and wills herself to feel more numb, more quickly.

'Are you ready?'

Both the girls say no, shaking their heads with broad grins on their faces.

'Okay. Everyone knows there are a lot of old ghosts here. From *la révolution*, ghosts who stayed close to their bones. Maybe you hear them already, whispering in the wall.'

Billie strains to listen to the quiet, to find sounds in it.

'But the old ghosts are gentle, they only want to talk. There is another ghost down here, a ghost who is not so friendly.'

Noémie's telling has a rehearsed feeling to it, the beats landing in a fluid manner that tells Billie she has told it, or heard it, many times before now.

'I am talking about the ghost ... of the cameraman.'

At this, all the teenagers un-tense and nod together. They know this one. Noémie looks to Billie, Tom and Wayne to confirm that they do not, and carries on.

'One day a few years ago, some guys were exploring a deep part of the tunnels that people do not go to so often. There are many bones there, and not so much art on the walls. A place that does not belong to humans.'

Billie's eyes stray reflexively to some of the larger graffiti lit up by the few candles still burning, and she reads the single word 'sexe' inflated in balloon letters.

'They were talking there and they found something on the ground, a bit hard to see by some rocks. It was a video camera, like a big, old one.' Here Noémie lifts both her hands to encase a square of air in front of her face.

'It has no battery, so they don't think about it so much, they pick it up, go to have their little party and come back to the city. Then they find something to charge it, and they see the whole tape is full up. Why did somebody leave it behind? But then ... they watched the tape.'

Wayne grimaces and makes a gesture like he's refusing an offer of food he finds disgusting.

'It's black and white, and the date says it's in the nineties. On the tape was only film of the catacombs, and sometimes you see the hand of the man holding the camera. He is on his own, exploring. He films the graffiti, *les chatières*, all just normal things. He does not say anything, only walks slowly. The only sound you can hear is his feet. Then the film stops, and starts again. Now he is in a different part. There are bones everywhere. He picks up a skull that is half broken. You can hear him breathing now.'

Billie is very glad that there being no signal down here means that nobody is going to try to make her watch this footage.

'He is walking on bones, and he is lost. Then, he starts to walk faster.'

'Noémie, you bitch,' says Wayne, his hands clamped to his cheeks.

'You can hear his breathing a lot now, and then he starts to run. He runs faster and faster, turning into new tunnels and going deeper and deeper and then ... '

243

Billie looks to Tom, gripping his beer tightly with his eyes wide. She surges with annoyance at him. Why are they here?

'... the camera drops. All you see is the man running away. Then nothing. The camera films the empty tunnel, until the tape runs out.'

The boy in the beanie grips one of the girls by the shoulders and shouts in her ear. She lets out a full, awful scream and turns to begin pummelling him with real anger while he keels over laughing and tries to protect his head with his arms.

'But who was he?' says Tom.

'Nobody knows. But some people say that if you go too deep in the tunnels, you can hear him running, and the closer he gets to you, the harder it is to breathe.'

There is a pause.

'You want more stories?' asks Noémie.

'Fuck no,' says Wayne, standing up decisively and shaking himself out a little, 'someone put some music back on.'

Tom and Billie end up next to each other relighting the candles. She feels a need to take Noémie down a peg, and take the sting out of her story by extension.

'She's a bit dramatic, isn't she?' she says quietly. 'With the code names and the rosary beads.'

'What rosary beads?'

'I don't think she likes me.'

Tom smiles.

'She's just like that.'

'Well, then I don't like her if that's just what she's like.' Billie feels the drink making her mean. 'That camera thing is obviously fake as well.'

Tom gives her an amused look.

'Well yeah, probably. But be nice, okay?'

Over near the edge of the wave, the goofy pair of boys are trying to rope Noémie into making a video with them, of some kind of kickline routine that doesn't go with the music. Tom goes over to join them. Their speaker has died, so they are playing it out of someone's phone now and it sounds even less like something worth dancing to. Billie sits down on the rock, lights up a cigarette and wonders how long the others are going to want to stay down here.

Wayne comes to sit next to her. He lights a cigarette of his own and lets the smoke unfurl from his mouth.

'I mean, I didn't think there would be cool people down here, but I didn't expect them to be quite this uncool.'

Billie laughs a little. They watch the tall girl take a picture of the girl with the buzzcut, hunkered in front of the wave in a rapper's squat.

'God, Instagram really has ruined the whole world, hasn't it,' Wayne says. The girl changes pose to sit in profile on the rock ledge behind her. 'She looks cute though.'

Billie nods. Faintly, she becomes aware that she can hear more voices approaching the cavern, low and male.

'She does.'

'If it's not weird of me to ask,' Wayne says, angling his body towards her, one leg crossed neatly over the other, 'how do you think Tom is?'

Billie looks across the space at Tom, who is swigging from a can and grinning at something Noémie has said.

'It's not weird. I don't really know,' she says.

'Does he ... he doesn't talk to me very much about

245

stuff but he must be feeling all kinds of ways about his – your dad.'

She takes a sip of her beer and watches as a small group of young men comes into the cave to join them. They lumber into their own corner to sit down. They look like the same group who were watching the guy with the synthesiser, but he doesn't seem to be with them any more.

'Yeah. He's always been a little freak.' The comment feels too harsh as soon as it's out of her mouth. 'Or he's always seemed kind of ... beyond, emotionally. Like things don't seem to upset him. But yeah, I think he's okay. He hasn't really said.'

She takes a drag of her cigarette and watches the smoke coil in the still air.

'Okay. Well yeah, I hope he changes his mind about the funeral. That's the kind of thing you could really regret, right?'

Billie doesn't follow him.

'In what sense?'

'If he doesn't go.'

Adrenaline races down her limbs. Something falls through inside her, like a trap door beneath her lungs is flapping wide on its hinges.

'He said he's not going to come?' she says.

Wayne switches tack noticeably.

'I'm sure it was just chat to get me to stop asking him about it. Sorry, I thought you guys already—'

'No, yes. He told me.'

'Okay phew. God, I thought I'd really ... yeah.'

Wayne exhales with obvious relief. She watches the smoke dissipate in front of them.

'Well, it's nice that he has you to look out for him. And me, but I'm only me and you know, you're family which is ... yeah. Anyway sorry, blah blah blah. I'm gonna find out from Noémie if there's anywhere not gross to pee down here.'

Wayne gets up. She meets his eye and he pauses.

'Are you ... you're all right?' he says.

She makes herself smile, and he turns to leave her. Billie finds herself standing too. She brings her can to her lips, drains it in several long gulps and drops her cigarette on the rock ledge. With her heart clenched in her throat, she turns around and walks out of the cavern.

22

Tom and Nour like to meet her friends in a bar near the Panthéon. One of them works there, which means that sometimes, towards the end of the evening, they get free rounds of whatever stock hasn't sold well that month. Tom doesn't hear English here, and this gives him a contented feeling, a confirmation of his place in what he thinks of as the real Paris. Wayne and Matthias occasionally join them for the final drinks of a night out, and he likes it when this happens because he can feel like an integral cog in the machinery of the occasion, rather than a spare part.

When they had first started hanging out with Nour's friends, they had spoken mostly in English on his account. He felt guilty about stifling their conversation and asked them to speak French. The first few weeks were tiring, Tom always hobbling a few beats behind. By the time he was sure enough of what was being said, and had formulated a response in his mind, the conversation had moved on. He did a lot of smiling and laughing at other people's jokes. But he was getting better each time at following along, and it felt like an important step into Nour's life to be speaking her language rather than his. He likes watching her with her friends, seeing her personality shift into a different register than when they are alone. He takes photographs of them all together, and imagines looking back at them in a decade's time. In these imaginings, Tom and Nour are older and wearing different clothes, but they are still sat on the same bed in her little apartment.

The more he drinks, the less the words resist him. He can draw conversation fluidly from some wellspring in his mind, or he notices the mistakes he's making less, until he stumbles over into the blurred and swaying landscape in which he can't speak much of anything. It means he is frequently a good five drinks down by the time he and Nour wend their way home. When Nour is drunk, she's boisterous and keen to argue, leaning forward with one elbow on the table to count out her points on her fingers for whomever she disagrees with. He can see that her friends have learnt how to defuse her, to talk her back down into happy conversation, but Tom enjoys it. To him, she is the protagonist in any scenario, and he likes for other people to see her that way too. He likes to see her triumph.

One evening a few weeks after the Notre Dame fire, at the end of another expansive night at the bar, Tom sits on the bed in Nour's apartment and focuses on removing his jacket. The buttons are slipping away from his fingers as he tries to prise the stiff, cold denim off them. He feels loose and ready to sleep. He tells Nour that he hopes one day his French will be good enough for him to feel that he belongs in France. She suppresses a smile.

'What makes you think you will get to feel like you belong in France?'

He's caught off guard.

' . . . because I'm here, I guess. And I want to be here.'

She nods, still smiling to herself.

'Well, why do I have to stay where I was born?' he says. 'Why does it make sense for anybody to be anywhere?'

'That's nice for you, to be able to think of it that way. You belong where you want to because you're a white guy.'

'I didn't mean it like that.'

'No,' she says lightly, 'you did. There is no other way to mean it.'

'I don't know.' He shuffles out of his jacket and hurls it into the corner where the rest of his things tend to lie in a crumpled pile. His mind drops him back into a conversation they always seem to be dipping in and out of having after the first few rounds of drinks. 'I just think a lot of people got so upset about leaving the EU because they don't get to move to Berlin or whatever any more, which they were never going to do anyway.'

'But you're the same, you also think you shouldn't be restricted where you live.'

Tom takes a swig from last night's glass of water, still sat beside the bed. 'All right, fine. But at least I actually moved away.'

'So what, you did it. That doesn't make you a better person.' There's a little mischief in her voice, but he's too tired to have this debate. In any case, he thinks it does make him a better person.

'I know you think it does,' she says. Her face relaxes. She shrugs. 'Maybe you're right.'

Tom likes this about her, too, the ease with which she can step out of the ring of an argument before the bell has rung, if she doesn't think the fight is worth her time. Nour goes back around the corner and leaves him turning his attention to his shoelaces. In the other part of the room, he can hear her by the sink, slugging some water and breathing out into the glass with a low, piston sound. There is a clicking as she looks at things on her laptop. Then, a gasp catches in the back of her throat.

'What?' Tom calls.

He hears Nour stomp towards him and she reappears, her face like a lit bulb.

'They said yes to my story! They're going to publish my story!'

He lights up too.

'Who did?'

She does a small, frantic pogo dance saying the name of a magazine he sees her read sometimes, and then bowls him onto his back on the bed to bury her face in his neck, still wriggling with excitement.

'That's great,' he says into her hair. Heavy liquid is sloshing around in his head. 'I didn't know you'd submitted something.'

She hoiks herself back onto her hands, rearranges her fringe and looks at him sheepishly.

'I wanted to wait until maybe they would say yes,' she says, 'to tell you.'

He smiles at her.

'Well, it's a lovely surprise.'

She shuffles off the bed and goes back into the other part of the room, reappearing with her open laptop cradled in her arms. She sits back down on the end of the bed beside him.

'It's another surprise actually,' she says, holding the computer pointed towards herself so that its screen lights up her chest. She turns it around to face him, and he sees a Google document. At the top of it, he reads a word count, Nour's name and the title: 'Vénération'. Her head hovers above the screen, grinning.

'I was thinking so much about what you told me, about you at the church and those boys—'

Tom breaks eye contact with her and begins to look properly at the screen in front of him.

'—and I got inspired to write a story, I sat down and it all came out of me in only a few hours.'

Tom's heart makes itself known in his chest. He reaches out two fingers to scroll through the text. He wishes he hadn't drunk so much and could focus on the words. But even sober, Nour's written French has always been just beyond his comprehension level.

'You wrote about me?' His voice sounds strained. Her smiles wanes.

'Well, it's not the same. I was inspired by it, by what you said. I changed things.'

Panic tingles in his hands and his heart rises to a pound.

'I don't . . . '

He knows this is not the right way to react to this news. It's good news, and he tries to grip onto that thought. But he can't calm himself down.

'I don't like that you did that. It's not—'

He gets up from the bed and his blood flushes through him. He stands uselessly, not looking at her. Then he meets her eyes and she looks crestfallen, but he can't tell yet if she's disappointed with herself for her mistake, or with him for his reaction.

'It's not your business,' he says. She bristles, and he knows who she is disappointed with.

'What's not my business? I wanted to make something from those feelings we talked about. Because everyone feels things like that. You don't own feelings.'

She is getting into her stride now. A stone of anger drops inside him, making a familiar ripple in his stomach.

'This is actually not about you, it's about my work,' she says.

'Is my dad in it?'

She looks away, her face contorting.

'I'm so excited about this, Tom. I thought you would be excited.'

He takes the laptop from her and tries to read the story, but he can't parse the sentences. He feels trapped, locked on the other side of a door from the document in front of him. He tries to slow down, but his eyes keep leaping forward as he scrolls to land on the key words he is most afraid of finding. He sees the words for church, father and shame.

'It's not yours,' he says, as she snatches her laptop back from him and snaps it shut.

Tom thinks back to the afternoon when he told her this memory and feels a new surge of anger, from a slightly different source. The mistake had been his, for giving her the power to bring his past into their present. He can see colour rising in her face as she grips the computer in her lap.

When Nour speaks, there is a harshness in her voice, one that lets him know she is ready to raise it.

'So you can do what you want, yes? Go wherever you want, take whatever you want. But not me.'

He is confused and tries to relate what she's saying now to the situation at hand. He tries to re-read his memory of the conversation they were having before they were talking about the story, but he can't find her anger in it, and can't in fact call many of the things either of them said to mind clearly. Had she been annoyed with him? His head spins as he tries to accelerate his drunken brain to meet the task. His voice comes out louder now.

'I don't—' His frustration at not being sober enough to think clearly is clotting into something nastier. '—we're talking about you taking – making my ... my life other people's business—'

'But why will people think it's real? Nobody will know.'

Nour continues to argue her corner, but he is not listening because he is focusing so intensely on fighting back the tide of anger. He cannot let her see it. He can feel her hardening, having enough of him now. They fight for what feels to Tom like a long time, Nour going into full and repetitive detail about how disappointed she is with him and Tom saying as little as possible, not trusting himself to speak.

'Why are you being so crazy about this?' she finally shouts, trying to get something substantial out of him, and she turns away in exasperation when he doesn't respond. Tom works to contain himself, to feel that this doesn't matter, that the two of them and the life they are making together are the things that matter.

She turns back to him, the anger and the drink full in her face.

'Well, now I know where you get it from.'

A sudden heat rushes through his body. He can still see, but something has disconnected and he feels unable to process the images. Some force outside of himself takes the reins, and wrenches his tongue backwards in his mouth, drawing a pool up from his glands, and he realises what his body is telling him to do. At the last moment, he manages to divert the urge, and he spits on the floor at her feet.

Their eyes meet and hold them there together for one shocked second in which Tom sees a life of dealing out violence unfurl before him like red carpet. Then he breaks her gaze and horror crashes over him. He needs to leave.

Nour begins to cry as Tom snatches his coat from the pile and throws himself out of the front door of her flat, his whole body trembling. He puts a hand over his mouth and grips to hold himself together until he has stumbled to the bottom of the stairs and burst out into the street, people and traffic streaming past him, and here, he lets out a deep, low sob, because he has been seen for what he really is.

23

Wayne returns from around the corner of the next tunnel, pinching the lid of a large plastic bottle with pale yellow liquid sloshing inside it, his face creased with disgust. The new group of guys let out a braying noise at the sight of the urine, and Wayne gives them a narrow smile. Tom puts out a hand for the bottle, and once he's given it to him Wayne flexes his hands repeatedly with desire for a sink before wiping them on his trousers.

'Surely we can pee on the ground,' Tom turns and says to Noémie, who looks up with irritation from her conversation with the girl with the buzzcut.

'No, you pee in the bottle,' she says.

Tom goes around the corner into an empty tunnel. The bottle is unpleasantly warm in his hand as he pees into it. When he has zipped himself up, he comes back into the cave and Wayne looks at the now very yellow liquid with exaggerated disapproval.

'Wow. Drink more water.'

'It's all very well not leaving anything behind,' Tom says to Noémie, 'but I'm not carrying this around.'

She rolls her eyes and gestures for him to give it to her.

'You're disgusting,' says Wayne admiringly.

Tom thanks her, and she shifts herself onto her feet to put the bottle next to her bag.

'Now I need to go,' she says, grabbing another empty plastic bottle and ducking out of the room.

A slightly obscene image occurs to Tom of the kind of pose Noémie is going to have to manoeuvre herself into in order to aim her pee into the bottle, and he wills it out of his mind. He turns to look around the cave. It feels busy. The new group have made themselves comfortable, opening drinks and spreading out on the ledge.

Then, he notices.

'Where's Billie?'

Wayne turns to look as well.

'Wasn't she with you?' Tom says to Wayne. He spins himself in a slow full circle to scan for her.

'That's so weird, she was sat there like … yeah, a few minutes ago,' Wayne says.

Tom calls her name, surprised at how quickly his voice sounds agitated. The noise of the other people in the cave dips in its wake, but there's no reply.

'Did you see where my sister – our friend, the other girl – did you see where she went?' Tom asks the teenagers. They all shake their heads or shrug with mild concern on their faces. He catches the eye of one of the new guys sitting on the far side of the cave.

'Did you – *avez-vous vu une fille*? Avec … des—' he's too

257

flustered to think of the word for frizzy hair, so he makes a curling motion with each of his forefingers next to his temples. The guy looks nonplussed.

'Crazy?' he says in English.

'Shit,' Tom says to himself, turning away from the stranger for another pointless look around the space. He sees the bright purple backpack propped up against the ledge and can't decide what it means that it's still here but she isn't.

'She did seem a little bit ... I don't know,' says Wayne quietly. Tom rounds on him.

'A bit what? Where did she go?'

'I don't know! I don't know, we were sat there talking about you and the funeral and then like, the importance of family ... '

Wayne trails off and Tom's blood thumps. Surely not.

'What about me and the funeral?'

Wayne gives him a nauseated look.

'That you didn't – that you aren't maybe going—'

Tom turns and strides off towards one of the cavern entrances, Wayne trailing him.

'She said that you talked about it!'

'Stay here,' Tom says, turning to direct the order right into Wayne's face. His voice is quiet but the force of his anger still roots Wayne to the spot. Tom turns back to keep walking, and then changes his mind.

'Or go look another way.'

Wayne nods forcefully and casts around for a path to follow. Tom enters the tunnel and tries to steady his breathing. He pulls his phone out of his pocket as he walks. He looks at it dumbly, knowing there will be no signal, and no message from her. He registers that it's half past two in the morning. They had walked for longer than he thought to get here. He reaches a fork in the pathway and calls out his sister's name, listening keenly for her voice through the echoes of his own. Nothing.

He picks the left fork and gets a dozen or so metres down it before he realises that he's going to need to find his way back here. He stops still to think. He reaches both hands into his jacket pockets for inspiration and wraps his fingers around the packet of Haribo bears. He tears it open, drops one on the ground and keeps walking. Every time he rounds a bend or chooses between turnings, he drops one behind him, careful to avoid losing them in the cloudy water pooled all over the tunnel floors.

With each step further down into the network his anger at Wayne and his anger at Billie for walking off is replaced by fear, amplified louder and louder in his body by the guilty knowledge that he was the one who brought her here in the first place. He tries not to imagine Billie's conversation with Wayne, how her face will have looked while he was speaking, but the image keeps forcing itself on him.

Tom walks, picking up speed, and the graffiti peters out. He calls out occasionally and his nerves jangle with the silence these calls bring back to him. His shoes, which were beginning to dry out, start to seep water onto his toes again as he reaches longer, unavoidable patches of water. He thinks to look down and check for footprints, training his headlamp at the ground ahead. To his surprise, there are some, zigzagging away in front of him. Tom can't be sure they're hers. She's wearing his shoes, but he can't picture their soles, what they would look like imprinted in dirt.

Tom follows the footprints as far as they go, but before long he reaches dryer parts of the tunnels again and they vanish. In all three forward directions, there is no sign of her. Surely she cannot have got much further than this. He drops another sweet, turning his head torch towards it to see it gleam like a jewel in the dust, and chooses the leftmost of three forks. Each turn he takes tightens the feeling that he is being pulled in two directions, back to the safety of the group and forwards to find Billie. He had expected to find her almost immediately, somewhere just out of sight but within earshot. But he will find her, and he will find the right thing to say. He'll explain himself and everyone will say sorry. He cycles through these thoughts in his head as he walks, hoping to make them true by their repetition.

At the top of an alleyway streaked with painted stick figures dancing, Tom turns into a cavernous room. And here, finally, he sees Billie. She is swaying a little on her feet, clutching a can too hard, and gazing at the rock face. For a moment, Tom is also distracted by what she's looking at. Someone has carved the facade of a cathedral out of the cave's wall. Its alcoves and spires are thrown into deep and overlapping shadows by the combined power of their head torches. Relief washes through him. Billie turns around, a placid look on her face.

'You scared the shit out of me,' Tom says, his fear congealing into anger again. 'I thought something had happened to you.'

She raises her eyebrows in a performance of surprise.

'Oh? Well look, I'm fine.'

There's a wild glint in her eyes, and something confrontational about her stillness.

'Come on,' he says, half turning to lead her back the way he came.

She doesn't move.

'No.'

'What do you mean no, let's go.'

'I don't want to.'

He's irritated now. He wishes he'd brought Noémie with him, for backup as much as for her map. 'Don't be stupid, we have to go back or we'll get lost.'

'I don't care,' she says. There is rage simmering in her voice along with the alcohol. 'You always do whatever the fuck you want, right? I can do that too.'

He wants to kill Wayne.

'Billie, this isn't—'

She holds his gaze as a manic smile splits her face. Then she turns on her heel and runs.

Tom is so stunned that it takes him a second to register that he needs to chase her. He rounds the corner and for an agonising moment he can't see her any more, but he can hear her footsteps pounding away up a passage to his right. He pursues her, their head torches making the tunnel walls flash maniacally.

He calls her name, dodging jagged outcrops of rock as they swerve deeper. He can't tell if he's gaining on her. Billie's fast, flailing forward into the dark, absorbing each trip into her crazed forward momentum. Then she rounds a bend in the tunnel and her feet slip out from under, sending her crashing into the dirt. She doesn't try to get up. Tom comes to a halt over her, heaving his breath back into his chest.

'What the fuck is wrong with you,' he pants, and she rounds

on him, lifting her face from the floor. He can see now that she's crying.

'No,' she bares her teeth, 'what's wrong with *you*?' She drags herself onto her feet from all fours, and straightens up, covered in streaks of powdered limestone.

'So you're not going to come to the funeral.' She smears a tear across one of her cheeks with the back of her hand.

'I don't know what Wayne said—'

'No, of course you're not. It makes perfect sense!' she says, sweeping her hands into the air in celebration of how much sense it makes. 'God forbid you should do one fucking thing for somebody else. God forbid you should take some responsibility for anything.'

'I didn't mean for him to – I didn't mean I'd decided anything,' he says, and it sounds weak.

She casts her arms around her in despair, looking at the tunnel around them.

'Why are we down here? Why would you bring me down here?'

'I thought you wanted to come! I—' He looks at the lowering rock and puddles of dirt and has to admit to himself that it's a fair question. '—I don't know, I thought it might be distracting.'

She gives him a grim look.

'That's all you do. Distract yourself.'

He squares up to meet her stubbornness.

'Look, we can talk about this all you want, let's just get back to the others.'

'You're a liar,' she screams at him, long and loud, holding the final word until she runs out of breath to sustain it. The echoes clang in the air and make Tom's heart start to slam against his ribs.

'You won't talk to me. You never talk to me.' Billie's voice is much quieter now, croaking and exhausted. She slides down the wall of the tunnel and comes to rest with the heels of her hands pressed on her eyes. He wants to get her out of danger, but he doesn't know what to say to get her there.

'What do you want me to say?' Tom asks with exasperation, and she laughs into her wrists. He looks for something simple and true. 'I don't . . . I didn't want to go.'

'What if it didn't matter whether you wanted to go?' Her voice starts to break again but she doesn't let it. 'What if the point of you coming was to be there for me and Mum?'

'Okay, yes, I'm sorry, please let's do this later,' he says, reaching out a commanding hand to pull her back up. She sits motionless.

'Billie,' he shouts, hating the sound of his own raised voice but desperate now to shake her out of it. She turns her face up towards him, and in her fury she looks so much like she did as a child that it takes him aback.

'Let's go now, please,' he says more gently, jerking his fingers into the palm of his outstretched hand. Billie doesn't take it, but gets to her feet herself, wincing a little and touching her leg.

'Is your leg—'

'I'm fine,' she snaps, brushing dirt off her sleeves. 'Go on then.'

Tom turns around, his breath coming more easily again. They begin to walk back through the tunnels, slowly and methodically. He is able to follow Billie's erratic footprints back as far as the cathedral room, and he follows his sweets from there. As they go, he picks up each Haribo bear from the ground, partly with Noémie's warnings about litter in mind and partly to ensure that they don't somehow end up doubling back on themselves and following the bears in a loop. Billie's silence is heavy and pointed behind him. He's sure that she is intentionally kicking water up the back of his legs when they reach puddles, but he decides not to say anything. He needs to get her back to the group.

Because Tom has been listening out for the echo of talk and music, their sudden arrival back at the mouth of *la plage* comes as a shock. As they round the corner, he stops short and hears Billie behind him do the same. It is the same cavern, but now the wave crashes down on an empty room. There's nobody here.

Billie looks at Tom.

'Where are they?' she asks.

He plainly cannot answer this question, but she doesn't know what else to say. She feels more sober with each minute but even so, she wishes that it would happen faster. She is beginning to understand exactly how stupid it was to leave the cave. Tom swears under his breath as he walks further into the space, looking around for an explanation. The tea lights all remain in place. A handful of them are still burning.

'Where did they go?'

'I don't know,' Tom says, and the panic Billie can hear under his irritation sends a cold rush down her back. She supposes that she had wanted to scare him when she left the cavern, but not this much.

There are clusters of cans dotted around the ledge. Billie's backpack is sat slouched where she left it. She goes to pick it up and swings it onto her shoulders. In one corner, over where the teenagers had stashed their bags, there is now a small pile of items heaped on top of each other. As Tom goes to shout for Noémie and Wayne down each of the tunnels that leads off the cave, Billie approaches the pile. There are some crisp packets, cigarette butts and two plastic bottles of yellow liquid. Tom comes over.

'I don't understand,' he says. 'Why would they leave?'

'They left all this rubbish,' says Billie, and they both look down at it. Billie thinks about how unlikely it is that Noémie would have willingly left this behind. She doesn't want to voice any of the thoughts that follow on from this fact. Tom turns away from the pile and goes back to storming from each tunnel entrance to the next, as though doing so will produce Wayne and Noémie, hiding somewhere just out of sight. Billie sits down on the ledge to steady herself. As they acclimatise to finding themselves alone, Billie's anger with Tom returns. Even before he speaks, the agitation in his movements tells her that the feeling is mutual.

'For fuck's sake, Billie, they've gone.'

'I can see that.'

'Why did you run off? How fucking stupid can you be?' Tom says, his voice raised and bouncing unpleasantly off the rock. She feels renewed for the fight.

'I left because I found out my brother wasn't planning to come to our father's funeral.'

'Fine, I'll come,' he says, dismissing the conversation with a bat of his hand. 'I don't want to talk about it any more.'

'How gracious of you. Thank you so much.'

Tom clamps his jaw in irritation.

'I'm not having a fight with you. We need to find the others,' he says, turning his attention back to the emptiness of the cave. Billie isn't going to let him slip away.

'What gave you the impression that you could just choose not to come?'

She has finally pressed the right button and he turns back to her.

'I can choose. He doesn't get—' she sees him struggle, '—he doesn't deserve it.'

Billie gives an insincere laugh. 'You can't seriously be—'

Tom interrupts her, a new energy in his voice.

'Why did Mum go to Glasgow?'

There is a pause while Billie stares at him and seethes.

'Did you never bother to ask her?' she says.

'I'm asking you. Why did she go and move in with Helen?'

She is on fire with how self-involved he is.

'She'd had enough, it was all too—'

'He shattered her eye socket.'

Billie stops speaking. It takes her what feels like a long time to hear him. She does a frenzied search of her memories. She must have seen her mum soon after she went to Glasgow, but how long afterwards? Maybe they had only spoken on the phone. She doesn't know.

'She got in the car to drive to Helen's but the pain was so bad that she came off the motorway at Manchester and took herself to hospital. Where I went to meet her because she called me from A&E.'

Billie feels liquid. After a few moments trying to assimilate what he's saying, she asks, 'Why did no one tell me?'

Tom looks at her, his eyes cold.

'So you wouldn't have to know.'

Billie doesn't know what to do with her body. She thinks of holding her dad's hand, of sitting with him in the days after her mum left, his broken shape crumpled on the sofa in front of the television, and she thinks of him with his fist raised in fury, and she aches with the effort of keeping those two people separate.

'But he couldn't—' She tries to make it all right. '—it wasn't his fault.'

Tom turns away and hatred blooms in her.

'He was sick, Tom.' She can hear the emotion rising in her voice and she can't keep it down now. She's no longer at the wheel.

'So he said.'

There is a pause while Billie fails to collect herself.

'What are you—'

'I'm saying what is absolutely fucking obvious, that maybe the only thing that was actually wrong with him was that he was a bad person.'

The air rings and neither of them speak for a moment.

'You can't say that,' Billie whispers, shock shrinking her voice.

Tom lets out a desperate laugh.

'I can say whatever I want, Billie, because it doesn't matter any more, does it? We're never going to find out now, are we?'

'You don't—' She is reeling. 'He was better. He was doing better.'

'So what? He got married again, that doesn't mean he's not a piece of shit. And if he really was sick then why did the diagnosis change, how were we—'

Tom catches himself.

'No. I don't want to talk about it. I don't want to spend my life raking through it. I want to move forward. You want to live in a fucking museum to him.'

Billie looks at Tom, her face a dead weight.

'You're a piece of shit.'

He nods as she speaks, and she is thrown.

'Correct. I am also a piece of shit.'

Tom looks for a moment like a toddler does when they hurt themselves, his eyes wide and on the brink. Billie hasn't seen this coming.

'I'm—' he sobs, once and then again, looking around them for something to make them stop. He drags the inside of one elbow across his face to wipe his eyes, but then he leaves it there, as if he's trying to hide. Billie has never seen him like this.

'Tom,' she says, and he really starts to cry, sitting down on the ledge and burying his face in his hands. She doesn't know what to do. Billie has rehearsed having versions of this conversation with Tom many times in her life, under her breath after phone calls or in her imagination, face pressed in fury against the pillow in her childhood bed. It has felt inevitable that at some point these things would be said, and yet she can't believe that they have said them. But Tom did not cry in any of the rehearsed versions. She stands uselessly and watches, and then goes to sit next to him. She puts a hand on his back, which doesn't feel right but it feels more right than doing nothing.

'I'm sorry,' she hears him wail into his knees.

'Okay. I'm sorry too,' she says.

She knows that neither of them have the energy to explain exactly what they're sorry for. Now that they are no longer in the heat of the fight, their immediate situation closes in on them again. Fear creeps back up Billie's spine.

Billie lets him cry it out in his own time. After the crying stops, he stays slumped over in silence for a while. Then he wipes his face and gathers himself back into an upright position.

'What should we do?' she asks.

Tom frowns and closes his eyes. He puts his head in his hands again, but with purpose this time, cupping his face in thought. Billie searches her mind for anything useful and pushes away the ever more pressing images of what the consequences might be if they do the wrong thing. Her mind automatically goes to where she usually finds the solution to her problems, or distraction from them: her phone. But when she looks at the screen she is irritated at the reminder that there is no signal and that the phone is useless. Then she thinks again.

'I took photos. As we were walking.'

Tom doesn't look up from his hands.

'We can use the pictures to find the way we came in,' she says.

Tom sits up with force, his face splotchy and livid.

'We're not leaving this cave. This is absolutely basic, Billie, if you get lost, you stay where you are.'

She fights down the afterglow of rage she still feels from their earlier conversation.

'But I'll know the way back.'

'You can't know the way back, we walked for too long. And you're drunk.'

He rubs the sides of his face hard with both hands and gives a deep sigh.

'Why do you have to get so drunk?' he says quietly.

'I'm fine,' she says, because this is too big a question for now, 'but we don't know what . . . '

She takes a breath. She knows that once she says this out loud, it will be impossible to take it back. It will change the mood permanently.

'Maybe something bad happened to them here. And I don't want it to happen to us.'

Tom is angry again.

'Don't be so dramatic,' he says, but the last word comes out weakly. She sees how afraid he is.

'Well look, I don't want to sit here and find out, okay, Tom? Please? We need to get out of here.' She is trying to keep her voice measured and to sound reasonable, but the echo of it rings with fear. 'Please.'

The silence around them is huge.

'How many pictures?' he says. Billie gets out her phone, queasy at seeing the orange pill of the battery bar, and taps to her photo library. There are a dozen or so photos, colourful snapshots of wall, brightly lit backs of heads, rucksack straps straying into the frame. They look at them for a moment.

'Please, Tom,' Billie tries one more time.

She knows that his word is final in matters between them, as it always has been. He will have to decide. She waits.

'Okay,' he says eventually. 'If you're sure?'

It strikes her as an odd question because she could not be sure, but she feels the strength of his need for some kind of reassurance.

'Come on,' she says, standing up abruptly, seized by a renewed sense of how urgent it is that they leave this part of the tunnels. He stands too, and Billie walks with purpose towards the opening of the pathway they had first entered from.

'Was it—' Tom says.

She turns back towards him. He continues to vacillate for a moment and then nods.

'No, yes, you're right, it was this one.'

Billie walks on, phone in hand with the most recent picture on the screen, ready to cross-reference it with the walls. She knows that the map she's cobbled together is so insufficient as to be basically useless. She tries not to think about it. She scours her memory for images of the pathway, and finds little, but not nothing. Her phone has a compass on it which she thinks wildly about using for a moment before realising that their orientation would mean nothing to her. She wishes she had asked Noémie which direction they had been moving in, wishes she was the sort of person who cared about maps enough to have looked at them properly in the restaurant.

They come to the first fork and Billie's spirits lift. They turn left, into a low passageway she remembers ducking to enter. Tom follows.

The things he said about their dad are deafening. Billie feels somehow as if their conversation is still happening, that it's reverberating into the present moment. She's almost glad to have to do this navigation, to have something else so immediate on which to focus.

They emerge into a wider space and keep walking. She

hates the quiet around them, punctuated only by their own scuffling and splashing footfall, and feels a surge of affection for Wayne and his phone speakers. He must be somewhere further ahead of them, also making his way out of the tunnels, but she can't construct an image for what must have happened between now and the last time she saw him. There's nothing in her head but an ominous space where that image should be.

At the next fork, Billie is less certain. They've not yet reached anything that matches her pictures. She turns around and begins to step backwards uncertainly, waiting for her memory to slot in with what she's seeing. She doesn't meet Tom's eyes. There is a fragile thread of agreement between them not to speak their fears aloud, and she is careful not to be the one to break it.

She picks a path and they walk in silence for a while. At last, at the top of a long tunnel where they wade through ankle-deep water, Billie finds the numbers 1854 carved into one of the bricks at waist level, a brick that that appears in one of her photographs. She keeps going, spurred on by this confirmation that they've done the right thing. Over and over, new images of her mother repeat themselves in her mind, a kaleidoscope of black and blue. She recoils from it.

They walk and walk, and when they finally round a corner and find themselves stood in front of the carved cathedral, and Billie realises that they have been walking in circles, she lets out a cry and lowers herself to the ground.

Tom cycles rapidly through a sequence of feelings, and lands on resignation.

'I'm sorry, Tom,' Billie says to her knees.

He can tell that she is bracing herself for his anger, but when his voice comes, it's low and soothing.

'It's okay,' he says, squatting down to join her on the ground.

'I don't know where we are.'

'I know. It's okay, someone will find us.'

She scrapes herself around to lean against the wall, facing the building hewn into rock.

'We just have to wait,' Tom says, shifting his backpack around to his side so that he can reach inside it. He is compelled to improve their situation in even a small way. He pulls out a battered old cagoule, and hands one end to Billie to sit on, and spreads the other side out next to her.

'We'll just wait,' she replies, closing her eyes against the shadows.

He shuffles to sit beside her. They are silent for a long time, each of them guiding the other into breathing more slowly and deeply.

'I thought we would have more time,' Tom says eventually.

'Jesus, we're not going to die.'

'More time with him.'

'Oh.'

He wishes she hadn't voiced the possibility that they could die.

'More time for me to feel differently I suppose I mean,' Tom says. 'Or—' he's so tired. 'I don't know. I don't know what I meant.'

He thinks about the tunnels branching away from them into miles and miles of darkness.

'I don't know what I'm doing,' he says, feeling that this

273

is only the very beginning of what he wants to say, but also that it is the end. Billie doesn't say anything. He looks at the carving ahead of them in the rock, lit up too starkly in the cold glare of his head torch.

'Are there any candles left?' he asks Billie. She opens her bag and digs a hand around inside it. She comes up with two tea lights, their metal cases dented and their wicks flat to the wax.

'We should save the torch batteries,' he says, taking one from her and getting to his feet. He finds a lighter and goes over to the wall and picks a carved doorway to put his candle in. Billie gets up and joins him. The wick catches and the flame burns an unwavering column in the tunnel's still air. Billie holds out a hand for the lighter, and she closes her eyes slowly as she puts her own tea light in a hollow parallel to his own. The glow in the space is warmer now. They go back to their spot on the floor, and Tom's heart gallops in the moment after Billie switches off her headlamp, then slows again. He takes his own off and holds it in his hands, casting a low pool of light on the ground in front of them. He couldn't even begin to guess how long the battery lasts.

'This is insane, we can't just sit here,' Billie wails without warning, and the cavern echoes with the scuffle of her trying to get to her feet. He brings her back to the floor firmly.

'They will find us. All we need to do is wait.'

'Okay. Okay.'

She nods several times, convincing herself. He reaches to hold her in his arms, awkwardly and sideways at first and then more loosely as they relax into the stone. He feels her settle herself into his side.

'Do you think we should pray?' Billie asks, in a voice that sounds drained by crying and alcohol.

A single laugh of exhaustion deflates him.

'Stop it. We're fine.'

But as they sit there in silence, he decides to run the familiar words in his head, just in case.

After a long and featureless period of time, Tom is sure that Billie is asleep. Her breathing is slow and thick. He doesn't want to shift his body to check the time and wake her. He wonders if it is dawn yet on the surface, whether Wayne and Noémie have been able to alert whoever you alert to the fact that they are down here. He imagines the catacombs police, who appear in his mind as Met officers in waders, somewhere in the network, and wills them towards him. Billie swallows heavily and he realises that he never showed her the picture he took of her asleep the previous morning. Every so often, he is seized by a grip of panic that they should be looking for a way out, but he does not move. If you are lost, stay still. The swell of tiredness behind the adrenaline that is keeping him awake begins to drag on him. He must not sleep. The dark billows around them.

It must be hours later when he feels the first shift in the air. The energy of something that's not quite heat, a presence. There is something moving in the tunnel.

His heartbeat rises fast and he tenses. He thinks about waking Billie, thinks about whether he is definitely awake himself. The air creeps colder and his skin pricks sweat. He scrambles to press his hand against the ground, to anchor himself to it, and he feels a trembling that runs all the way through him.

And then, he sees it. It makes his breath leave his body and pins him to the rock, unable to do anything but stare in paralysed silence.

24

There is a cave under his bed. To get there, you have to push a laundry bin out of the way. One of the best things about the cave is that you can't tell it's there unless you already know. It's hard to be sure if his mum knows about the cave. He'll never ask her, because that would give the cave away. But so far it seems like she doesn't. When he puts things in the cave, nobody takes them out again. He can take something into the cave, like Buzz Lightyear or a bag of crisps, and it will still be there after days and days. This is what tells him that his mum doesn't know about the cave. He has to take them out himself. He's in charge of the cave, and what goes inside it.

The cave is the perfect size. The drawers under the bottom bunk don't reach all the way to the wall, like the bed itself does, and that's what creates the cave. It's good for crawling into. When you get to the end of the cave, you can either sit curled over with your head touching the mattress, or you can lie down. Lying down is more comfortable, and he likes to look at the wooden planks that hold the mattress up. He likes the way they smell woody, like a forest. There is a brown shape on the underside of the mattress halfway into the cave that's from a time when he wet the bed. It looks like the map to an island. The cave is the best place in the house, and he can't believe how cool it is that the best place in the house is a secret that belongs to him.

It's dark in the cave unless you take a light with you. He took a torch from a box downstairs the first time he saw the entrance to the cave, but people would notice if the torch went missing for a long time and the cave might be found out that way. Now, he takes a light he got given for his birthday, a plastic ball on a stand covered with coloured circles that spins around and makes disco lights when you have batteries in it. It's better than a torch, and nobody minds when he moves it from its usual place. When the disco light is in the cave, he imagines he's doing magic in there.

Sometimes, when they need to get away, he lets Billie come in the cave with him, which makes it a little cramped. She's three, so she's not that fun to talk to, and she doesn't know to respect the cave. He doesn't want to be in charge of her too often. She's got sweaty little hands and she puts food in his hair. But he likes having someone to be older than sometimes, to know more than.

Today is a day when he lets Billie in the cave. He always makes her put her hands over her eyes while he moves the laundry bin and leads her inside, or she'll know where the cave is and want to go in there all the time. She's small enough to stand up in the cave, which makes him a bit jealous. He tells her things to draw, and she puts a piece of paper up against the wall to draw them. Sometimes the pen gets on the wall if he doesn't watch her properly, but it doesn't matter in the cave. If she cries in the cave, it's very loud, so he has to make sure she stays distracted from whatever else is going on in the house when she's in the cave with him. He sings songs that he knows she knows, songs from *Aladdin* and, in an emergency, when she is really distracted by the shouting and screaming, he will sing that 'I'm Blue' song, and she likes to singalong with the *da-be-dee* bits. This is really nice of Tom because he hates that stupid song.

It's easy to imagine that they're the only people in the world, when they're in here. He thinks about what it would be like if, in a few weeks, the millennium bugs destroy every thing on the planet, and because they're in the cave, they survive. Only him and her, and Buzz Lightyear, for millions of miles all around. He looks at her, with her big curly hair that she has to brush out of her eyes all the time, her fat cheeks. Sometimes the thought of it being them alone scares him, but more often, it doesn't. He thinks he could do it, if he had to. He thinks he could take care of her.

25

Billie looks at herself in the mirror. She looks fine. She's wearing a dress she originally bought for work, a black shift with short sleeves and a rounded white collar. She stopped wearing it to work because it makes her look childish, but today that could be an advantage. It would be nice if people treated her like she needed to be looked after. She had thought about wearing something else for the morning, and leaving it until the last moment before she has to leave the house to put on the dress, but when she woke up, she saw that it was futile. The day only had one purpose.

She's exhausted in a way that runs deeper than lack of sleep. She has wondered in the past few days if she left some crucial part of herself down in the tunnels. The first thing she had asked the paramedics for, when the sounds of shouting voices had eventually found their way to where they were sitting, was the time. She was very thirsty, with hunger gnawing behind it, but the most important thing she wanted was to know how long it had been. They had been underground for over eighteen hours. Near enough a whole day passed on the surface without them, and although it's now been a week since, and she has done little else but sleep, she still feels the loss of that day like jet lag.

They have arranged to meet at King's Cross and travel up to Palmers Green together. The funeral will be held at three, out of mercy to Mary-Jean, who hasn't had time to adjust to the time difference. She thinks of her mum and Helen, who arrived late last night to stay with a friend. She wonders what they're talking about now, over their breakfasts, on the other side of the city. Maybe they're not talking at all, spoons clinking against bowls in the quiet. She and Tom have agreed not to tell her about the catacombs, and although Billie knows that this is the kind choice, she wishes she weren't hiding anything additional today.

Laura has gone out to yoga and Bethan must still be asleep. They will both come to the funeral with her, something they assumed without her asking. She'll be relieved not to be alone later on, but for now, in the clean light of the early morning, she's glad to have the flat to herself. She drifts into the kitchen and finds that Laura has left her a bunch of flowers and a Danish pastry in a brown bag mottled with grease. It's uncharacteristically thoughtful, and again the abnormality of the day grips Billie's throat. In a drawer under the kettle, she finds a pad of paper. She sits down, pushing the lilies further up the table, and places her phone next to the pad to copy out the poem. She writes slowly and double spaced. She found it on a website called dignityfunerals.com. There were pages and pages of poems, some from the perspective of the dead person, some dozens of verses long, all in a sing-song rhythm that seemed ill matched for the occasion. She couldn't imagine saying any of them. But she has to say something and she couldn't find her own words, and so she chose somebody else's. The author of the poem is anonymous, and it begins:

> Think of me as one at rest,
> for me you should not weep,
> I have no pain, no troubled thoughts,
> for I am just asleep.

She chose it because it's not too long, or too short, and because that actually is a nice way to think of him. She knows that she will see his coffin, and she prepares herself to imagine that he is only sleeping in there, snatching a warm, dark nap out of the day.

She finishes writing and looks up to see that one of the flowers has dropped its stamen on the table. When she picks it up, it leaves an orange stain on her fingers. She runs her hand under the hot tap, and stays there feeling the water for a long time after the colour has drained away.

Tom is wearing his suit, which looks more crumpled out here in the first hours of daylight than it had done in the apartment. He slept very little, only registering that he had fallen asleep at all by noticing that the time on his alarm clock had leapt forward, but he feels alive with nerves and caffeine. Usually, he sees this time from the other side. Today, as he passes little clusters of people hobbling home from nights out, he feels like he belongs to a different species.

Tom walks the half hour to the station, allowing each step

to be a small piece of evidence that he's on his way to the day being over. Eventually it is raining, but lightly enough to be almost pleasant, tiny pressures all over his face. He shares the streets mostly with supermarket delivery people, and the distant shunting and beeping sounds of trucks in reverse.

Wayne offered to accompany him to the station this morning, out of misplaced guilt as much as solidarity, Tom thinks. It hadn't been Wayne's fault, or Noémie's. When Tom and Billie had been brought back up to the surface, his phone had just enough battery to show him the barrage of text messages that each of them had sent him throughout the night on the chance that he might somehow receive them. The messages mentioned a stolen phone and a fight, and contained several frantic apologies and promises that Wayne was coming back to find them. Tom had been too tired to parse them then, but Wayne had later given him the full story in person. One of the guys in the new group made a homophobic dig at the girl with the buzzcut, a fight broke out and Noémie, fired up to defend her new friend was knocked to the ground. She hit her head hard. In the commotion that followed, the new group of guys snatched up their things and left the cave, taking one of the teenagers' phones with them. In Wayne's outraged telling, this was intentional. Tom focused on the dull throbbing in his temples as Wayne delineated how this phone had the teenagers' map on it, and exactly how the decision had been reached that, in order to get Noémie's head seen to by a doctor, they all needed to leave together, and someone would come back for Tom and Billie. Tom had listened to all of this feeling strangely uncurious about the details. When Wayne had finally purged himself of this account, he asked Tom what happened at their end, but Tom couldn't arrive at much more to say than that they waited, for a long time.

Noémie's concussion was only serious enough to win her a week off work instead of a stay in hospital. But even in convalescence it seems that she regularly gets up at a time so early it makes Tom feel ashamed, because she has already sent him a message this morning instructing him to be brave.

Tom has often heard people disparage the Gare du Nord, but he loves it, its grand, optimistic facade topped with statues whose hand-on-hip poses look oddly casual and impatient, as if they too are waiting for a train. Inside, the concourse is busy with people weaving around each other, or stood motionless, staring up at the departure boards. A number appears and half the crowd comes back to life, moving off in the same direction. Tom knows where his train goes from, so ignores the board and sits down on a bench set into the side of a news-agent. It's too early to eat, or even to think about eating later. He lets the energy buzzing in his legs from walking dissipate into the ground, and starts to feel tired. Announcements ring out and leave the sound of footfall and suitcase wheels rolling in their echo. The huge, empty air of the station above him makes him light-headed.

Tom thinks about home. Now that he's sitting here on the threshold, not in London but as close as he can be to it from here, he feels a kind of splitting in himself, a doubling. There's the person he is there, where he comes from, and the person he is here, where he came to. They jostle for primacy as he sits and waits. Tom is aware, in a peripheral way, that he should get up, check in, shuffle through the routines that stand between him and the train. But he doesn't move.

Tom pulls out his phone and, trying not to look at the previous texts in the thread, writes a message to Nour.

I miss you so much

He feels a painful thrill as he hits send, something he had not quite planned to do. He sits there pinned to the bench. There are any number of feelings this message might inspire in her, and thousands of places she could be when she receives it. He looks at his phone. Eight a.m. on a Sunday. She's probably still asleep, soft and warm and peaceful.

A part of him wants to tell her what he saw in the tunnels. But another part of him thinks that it's unlikely, even if she responds – even if the impossible series of miracles takes place and they end up together again – that he will tell her about it. In fact, he suspects that, if he said it aloud, his belief in it might shatter, and so he feels sure he won't tell anybody. It is enough for him to know what he saw, and to keep this secret with himself.

Another announcement brings his thoughts back to the time, and to the train. He really needs to get going now. But a strange incapacity has crept over him. Tom feels that, actually, to move wouldn't require so great an effort, and yet he doesn't. The minutes tick on, punctuated by more announcements, more transit of other people around him. As long as he sits in the station, there is the potential that he will get on the train and leave. But he does not move.

26

Tom has to learn his lines for some drama thing he's doing at school. It's not for his A levels and it's not for his drama school auditions either, it's another, third type of drama thing. Billie can't keep up. When she thinks about Tom doing A levels it's mad to her, because it means she's only four years away from taking her own. It's been a relief that Tom and her dad have had this to talk about for a few weeks. She doesn't mind that it doesn't involve her. She wishes she could do creative stuff, but when she's tried out little bits of acting in the mirror it looks like a hostage video.

The speech he's doing is from *Krapp's Last Tape*. Her dad helped Tom pick it. It's Krapp with a K and two p's, and she knows she should stop being so immature about it. It's Tom on his own playing this old man, and he's listening to an old recording of his own voice and sort of responding to it. But in the tape, the man is talking about listening to an even older tape. A tape within the tape. It's about memory, her dad had told her, which was obvious and she was annoyed that he thought she needed to have it explained. When Tom does it for real, he'll record the bit on the tape as well, but this afternoon they're quizzing him on his lines for the other bit, the bit he'll do on stage on the day. Tom had said he basically knew them, but he doesn't.

They're outside on the patio because her mum thinks it's a waste of having a patio if you don't go outside and use it when there's good weather. It's warm but not hot. Billie and her dad were taking it in turns to read the other lines for Tom while their mum makes potato salad. But now it's mostly her dad reading the lines while she watches, because Tom said she wasn't taking it seriously enough, which was true. Billie thinks you shouldn't put the word 'crap' in the title of your play if you want people to take it seriously.

It's a weird choice for Tom to do a speech by an old man. He doesn't know anything about being old. They don't even have any grandparents to ask about what it's like. But he's been practising the walk and it looks pretty good now, shuffling himself back and forth across the patio and holding the base of his spine like it might pop out. Billie gave it a try herself but everyone agreed that she looked too jerky.

They've moved the plastic table onto the patch of grass so that they can watch him like it's a stage. They're using the radio with the batteries taken out, so Tom can practise hitting the buttons like it's a real tape recorder without Capital FM starting to play. There's a bit at the beginning where he has to eat two bananas in a row and slip on the peel for no reason that Billie can work out. But they're not doing that bit now because it's hard to slip on grass. She thinks her life would be much easier if the thing she was good at and what she wanted to do when she grows up was slipping on a banana peel realistically. She's careful not to let her face show how stupid she thinks it all is, though. She doesn't want to break the spell of this afternoon, the good moods and nice weather. As they read, Billie fishes a bottle of nail polish out of her schoolbag, propped up against the table leg. This gives her an excuse to stay out there with them. Painting nails is kind of a creative thing.

Her dad is reading all the words of the tape, even though there are long bits where it's just the old man listening to his voice on the tape and they could skip forward to Tom's lines. He's sort of half-performing them, and he seems to be enjoying it, doing the little laughs and the pauses where the script says to do them. He's reading from his own book, one with all of Beckett's plays in, a big black brick that looks squashy like it's been dropped in a bath. Tom follows the words with his eyes on his own print-out copy of it. Billie has to look at her hands for each brushstroke, to stop mint green spreading into the grooves between her nails and skin, so she's mostly listening to them rather than watching. Their voices sound similar to each other, something she's not noticed much before. Her dad's has something crunchier about it, even though he's supposed to be reading the younger man's part. They should swap, and she almost says so before she remembers that the whole point is for Tom to learn the lines. She lifts her left hand to blow on her nails and looks at them both, their stocky frames and the brown curls, thinner and further back on her dad's head than on Tom's, but definitely the same. There's a bit in the tape lines about the man having his face in some breasts and she notices that Tom goes red but tries to pretend he hasn't. Her dad notices too, and smiles to himself, but he doesn't draw attention to it.

How Tom can remember any of this is a miracle to Billie. The lines don't make sense in the order they're in, and there are parts that get repeated over and over about which tape he's listening to. Tom keeps getting it wrong. He gets frustrated and they have to go back to the beginning, but her dad is being patient. His eyes are bright and he's here with them completely. There are several bits where Tom has to say the word 'spool' like it's really fun to say. They all try it out, Billie, her dad, Tom, and then her mum sends out a nice long 'spoooooool' that echoes out through the backdoor as she chops the chives. Everybody laughs at the same time. Billie finishes the second coat of colour on her first hand and admires her work, feeling joy spread in her chest. Her nails look good.

She has a feeling that she often has. She hates it, but she can't help it. At the beginning of anything good, she fast forwards in her mind to when it will be finished, and it makes the ending come sooner somehow. She sits on the patio chair listening to an airplane pass over them, and decides that this is a good moment to remember forever. And so she sits there, looking around at the laughing, open faces of her mum, her dad and her brother, trying to record the scene. This is possible. Here is the proof.

Acknowledgements

Thank you to early readers Lucia Osborne-Crowley, Allegra Le Fanu, Sophie Klimt and Elise Bell. I'm very lucky to have had each of your sharp eyes on it. To Lauren O'Neill for providing a safe space in which to be insane about trying to write a book. To Romp Club for watching terrible movies with me at least once a week throughout the time I was writing and providing escape from my own thoughts. I will remember watching *A Dog's Journey* until I am dead.

To my Låds, Emma Hall and Allegra Le Fanu, who have dragged me by my hair through this life. You'll notice Allegra gets thanked twice. If you knew her, you would understand that she's just that good. Thank you to the HGs, the best to ever do it. I'm sorry the first novel published by one of us was not the *Gossip Girl* tribute you guys each wrote a chapter of when we were thirteen. There's still time to get that out there. Think about it.

Thank you to my agent and friend Kat Aitken, for being intensely sound and wise, and for making it fun. Not everyone's agent will come round to their flat and drink so many margaritas that the TV gets smashed, and I think that's a shame. To my editor Rhiannon Smith, to Amy Perkins, Niamh Anderson, Emily Moran, Lucie Sharpe, Charlotte Stroomer and everybody who worked on the book at Little, Brown. To Talia Richard-Carvajal for everything. Everything, do you hear me! Thank you to Ben Lennon. To Brian O'Hagan, for our adventure underground. To Emily Forbes for sharing your stories of drama school. They were delicious in the way the best gossip is. And to my family: Jo, Laurie, Fred and Honor, for being mine. I love you!

Imogen West-Knights is a writer and journalist based in London. She writes most regularly for the *Guardian*, the *Financial Times*, the *New York Times* and Slate. She was shortlisted for the Portobello Prize 2017 and for the *FT*/Bodley Head Essay Prize 2018. She also writes video games. *Deep Down* is her first novel.